Integrative Psychotherapy

Acknowledgments

Work on this book was supported by the Marie-Curie Initial Training Network, "TESIS: Towards an Embodied Science of InterSubjectivity" (FP7-PEOPLE-2010-ITN, 264828).

Integrative Psychotherapy

A Feedback-Driven Dynamic Systems Approach

Günter Schiepek, Heiko Eckert, Benjamin Aas,
Sebastian Wallot, and Anna Wallot

With a foreword by David Pincus

Library of Congress Cataloging-in-Publication Data
information for the print version of this book is available via the Library of Congress Marc Database under the LC Control Number 2014958962

National Library of Canada Cataloguing in Publication Data
Schiepek, G. (Günter), author
    Integrative psychotherapy: a feedback-driven dynamic systems approach
/Günter Schiepek, Heiko Eckert, Benjamin Aas, Sebastian Wallot, and Anna Wallot.

Includes bibliographical references.
Issued in print and electronic formats.
ISBN 978-0-88937-472-0 (pbk.).--ISBN 978-1-61676-472-2 (pdf).--
ISBN 978-1-61334-472-9 (html)

    1. Eclectic psychotherapy. I. Eckert, Heiko, author II. Aas, Benjamin,
author III. Wallot, Sebastian, author IV. Wallot, Anna, author V. Title.

RC489.E24S35 2015   616.89'14   C2014-908462-5
                                                  C2014-908463-3

The present volume is an adaptation of G. Schiepek, H. Eckert, and B. Kravanja, *Grundlagen systemischer Therapie und Beratung: Psychotherapie als Förderung von Selbstorganisationsprozessen* (2013, ISBN 978-3-8017-2475-7), published under licence from Hogrefe Verlag GmbH & Co. KG, Göttingen, Germany.

© 2015 by Hogrefe Publishing
http://www.hogrefe.com

PUBLISHING OFFICES
USA: Hogrefe Publishing Corporation, 38 Chauncy Street, Suite 1002, Boston, MA 02111
                Phone (866) 823-4726, Fax (617) 354-6875; E-mail customerservice@hogrefe.com
EUROPE: Hogrefe Publishing GmbH, Merkelstr. 3, 37085 Göttingen, Germany
                Phone +49 551 99950-0, Fax +49 551 99950-111; E-mail publishing@hogrefe.com

SALES & DISTRIBUTION
USA: Hogrefe Publishing, Customer Services Department,
                30 Amberwood Parkway, Ashland, OH 44805
                Phone (800) 228-3749, Fax (419) 281-6883; E-mail customerservice@hogrefe.com
UK: Hogrefe Publishing, c/o Marston Book Services Ltd., 160 Eastern Ave.,
                Milton Park, Abingdon, OX14 4SB, UK
                Phone +44 1235 465577, Fax +44 1235 465556; E-mail direct.orders@marston.co.uk
EUROPE: Hogrefe Publishing, Merkelstr. 3, 37085 Göttingen, Germany
                Phone +49 551 99950-0, Fax +49 551 99950-111; E-mail publishing@hogrefe.com

OTHER OFFICES
CANADA: Hogrefe Publishing, 660 Eglinton Ave. East, Suite 119–514, Toronto, Ontario, M4G 2K2
SWITZERLAND: Hogrefe Publishing, Länggass-Strasse 76, CH-3000 Bern 9

Hogrefe Publishing
Incorporated and registered in the Commonwealth of Massachusetts, USA, and in Göttingen, Lower Saxony, Germany

Cover design: Daniel Kleimenhagen, Designer AGD

ISBNs 978-0-88937-472-0 (print) • 978-1-61676-472-2 (PDF) • 978-1-61334-472-9 (EPUB)
http://doi.org/10.1027/00472-000

Foreword

At the ripe young age of 23 I began my career as a therapist, an in-home youth social worker in rural Wisconsin, USA. Armed with a variety of systemic theory and techniques, I was ready to do some good in the world! My client was a sensitive, quiet 13 year-old boy. He had just been released from the adolescent psychiatric unit after he was found to be walking across the busy road near his mother's home hoping, perhaps, that he would be killed by a speeding car. He had been removed from his father's home a few weeks earlier, after years of repeated late-night sexual molestations after his father had been drinking. His mother reluctantly took him in – making a bed for him on her sofa. She complained of her own problems; she too was a survivor of childhood sexual abuse as well, along with each of her other two siblings, an older half-brother and a sister. She now had all three of her children to care for in her small apartment, and the return of her son made clear to her that all of her children had now suffered just as she had as a child.

My first concern in working with this young man and his family was not which approach to use. Like most therapists, I valued theory and technique – indeed I still do. Yet, most of us also come to realize that the use of technique always feels at least a little bit out of place; and in situations like these, it can feel downright disrespectful – especially in the face of such intense pain.

For most of my early career as a social worker, and later as a psychologist, these types of tough cases were my usual clientele. Driving home from work each day, I remember feeling like the little Dutch boy with his thumb stuck in the dyke, holding back some inevitable catastrophic flood, yet helpless to do anything really to fix the overwhelming circumstances that held my clients' problems in place. Over time, however, this metaphor has shifted, along with my basic understanding of cause and effect and, thus, my role as therapist. The key was in learning that what we do with our clients is far less important than *how we are* when we are working with them.

Still, modern culture mandates that we act in the role of professionals – and professionals *do* things. Given that the ancient title of "shaman" is not professionally credible in a modern society, we are by default most often considered to be "health care professionals." And so, we must dispense "treatments," with empirically tested techniques like: desensitization, "chair" work, or scaling questions. We nest these techniques in "approaches," with more than 400 of them at this point and more each day it seems, with such well-known initial as: CBT, IPT, EFT, and ACT. Each of these approaches are supposedly nested in "theories" of one variety or another that are really too numerous, fragmented, and jargon-laden to list.

These are the labels we use to define ourselves professionally. When interviewing for jobs, meeting other therapists, or in our first encounters with clients a typical question arises: "What approach do you use?" Or "What would you do with a typical client?" The appropriate answers I was trained to give, depending on who is asking, could include: "CBT," or "IPT," "brief psychodynamic work," or "systemic" therapy. Another option is the classic name drop, like "Ellis," "Luborsky," "Greenberg," "Hayes," "Minuchin," "Haley," or "Satir."

Most of us who are therapists know that the most honest answers would be: "There is no such thing as a *typical* client, and my aim in therapy is always to do as little as I possibly can." Technique is important; yet, just like a punch in a fight, technique is inseparable from its timing, its location, and its efficiency. One of many paradoxes in psychotherapy lies in the fact that the more we do as therapists, the more we lose sight of our clients, their experiences, and most importantly their own resources and capacities for self-healing.

In the text you are about to read, *Integrative Psychotherapy: A Feedback-Driven Dynamic Systems Approach*, the team of Günter Schiepek, Heiko Eckert, Sebastian Aas, Sebastian Wallot, and Anna Wallot take a major step toward resolving this, and numerous other paradoxes within psychotherapy. In this text, they demonstrate in clear and certain terms how the best scientific principles and the deepest clinical wisdom can be reconciled – resulting in an integrative "approach" to psychotherapy that does not need to pretend that approach or technique are the simple causes of our clients' recovery. This field-changing text goes further still – helping to reconcile the science-practice divide, turning rigid empirical vs. constructivist philosophies on their sides by making clear an essential truth: *reductive* science is fundamentally incapable of showing us how psychotherapy works. Instead, one must begin with the fact that biopsychosocial dynamics and psychotherapy each operate as irreducible and ever-changing systems.

The authors enter this process of psychotherapeutic reconstruction by analyzing the difficulty of defining systemic therapy based on any necessary or sufficient features; and by the end of Chapter 1, it becomes clear that all modern approaches can be considered to be systemic in one way or another. Indeed, attempting to define systemic psychotherapy appears almost as difficult as defining the broader class of psychotherapy itself. This text makes clear that within this fundamental challenge to define psychotherapies, one finds a number of complementary relationships, including: common factors and techniques, healer and patient, social and psychological, brain and mind. The science of psychotherapy is clear: We know that it works. Just don't ask us what *it* is.

In Chapter 2, the authors remove the proverbial "Emperor's Coat" on the various psychotherapy approaches – as the available evidence reveals that the distinctions among them are, at a minimum, not terribly important, and perhaps even fundamentally obfuscating of most scientific pursuits. They expand the important discovery of sudden gains over the past 20 years – building the foundation for a nonreductive approach to science in psychotherapy capable of integrating science and practice. Without the baggage of reductionism, they demonstrate how apparently confusing evidence on psychotherapy outcomes becomes clear – for example the strength of client and common factors and the relative weakness of technique when examined in isolation. For the first time that I am aware, we find here a scientifically grounded approach to psychotherapy that does not find it necessary to tell us what we need to do.

In Chapters 5 and 6 the authors explain the Synergetic Navigation System (SNS), grounded in the broader science of self-organization. This approach brings together our best practices in nonlinear science, experience sampling, and behavioral medicine, each applied to the process of psychotherapy. Well beyond the German mental health systems, the authors have created here a blueprint for modern mobile medicine that can serve as a model for the world.

Using a case example, they illustrate the therapeutic effects of daily feedback, and the idiographic map of therapy process and progress that is made available through the SNS. Enhancing the recursive, self-reflective power of traditional psychotherapy, their system is sensitive to the emergence of critical instabilities that are often hidden - particularly with clients who have adapted from an early age to hide their vulnerable feelings and social needs. At the same time, a new virtual, therapeutic triangle is developed where the therapist–client system can reflect on their own graphics of process and progress, grounded in the science of synergetic, self-organizing systems. Through the use of this technology, it is clear that each client creates an enhanced experiential relationship with the therapy process itself, increasing the forces of change via systemic factors – such as self-referential feedback, while also strengthening the stabilizing influence of the therapeutic relationship. Within this safe therapeutic cocoon, a variety of basic complementarities may be stretched and re-organized, including: experiential fusion and defusion, boundaries of self and object, emotional expression and regulation, coordination and autonomy, power and intimacy. Technique may then follow process, and be developed in collaboration – as it should in any good approach to treatment.

Finally, the authors take us for a peek into the future integration of psychotherapy with neurofeedback and other biologically-grounded approaches, each aimed at using the precision of synergetic principles to guide feedback procedures that can break up pathological rigidity emerging from over-synchronization.

Finally, we arrive full circle at the end of this text, with a clearer and broader definition of systemic psychotherapy. Through the use of synergetic science, these authors arrive at a fundamental truth shared by all healers, and taught by our greatest leaders, such as described in the following excerpt on Albert Schweitzer:

> I asked Dr. Schweitzer how he accounted for the fact that anyone could possibly expect to become well after having been treated by a witch doctor, he said that I was asking him to divulge a secret that doctors have carried around inside them ever since Hippocrates. "But I'll tell you anyway," he said, his face still illuminated by that half smile, "the witch doctor succeeds for the same reason that all of us succeed. Each patient carries his own doctor inside of him. They come to us not knowing that truth. We are at our best when we give the doctor who resides within each patient a chance to go to work." (Cousins, 1980, pp. 68–69)

David Pincus, PhD
Associate Professor of Clinical Psychology, Chapman University
Past President of *Society for Chaos Theory in Psychology and Life Sciences*;
Co-editor with Stephen J. Guastello and Matthijs Koopmans:
Chaos and Complexity in Psychology,
and Co-author with Anees A. Sheikh: *Guided Imagery for Pain*

Table of Contents

Chapter 1

Why Is It So Challenging to Define Systemic Psychotherapy?

In this book we would like to propose an integrative model of psychotherapy that encapsulates the different meanings of the term "integrative." We see the following dimensions to be of vital importance in this integration: science and practice (scientist-practitioner model); biological (e.g., neuronal), mental, and social functioning; the use of quantitative and qualitative data, of theoretical explanation and clinical understanding, the complementarity of nomothetic and idiographic approaches in psychology; and a clinical practice beyond psychotherapy schools.

One of the many reasons for this development is the shortcomings and limitations of the existing psychotherapy schools, e.g., the difficulties in defining them (see Chapter 1). Another reason is the empirical evidence that common and school-independent factors mainly contribute to the outcome of psychotherapy (see Chapter 2). Since the theory and methodology of nonlinear dynamic systems plays a crucial role in the theoretical foundation of our model, in a very general sense it is a *systemic* approach, but in a much broader sense. Whereas in the first chapter we refer to "systemic therapy" as a therapy school, later on in this book we will try to develop a general and integrative concept of psychotherapy. To start out on this challenging path, we use the therapeutic conviction of "systemic therapy" as a contrasting background for a new "Gestalt" which is outlined in this book. Using the example of the systemic therapy school it will become evident that there are neither necessary nor sufficient criteria for an appropriate definition. Our suggestion of an integrative psychotherapy will be systemic in the sense of using the nonlinear dynamic systems approach as a scientific framework and methodological base. Describing how this works is the aim of this book.

Systemic therapy and systemic counseling have become increasingly prominent in the past few decades. Along with behavioral therapy and psychoanalysis, the systemic approach is currently one of the three most common therapy schools in German-speaking countries. Systemic practice emerged at the beginning of the 1980s, though it could be argued that its roots and precursory concepts date back even further. Since then, other therapeutic approaches have been developed, such as awareness- or mentalization-oriented methods, schema therapy, and emotion-focused therapies (to name but a few). Systemic therapy no longer belongs to the new and fashionable approaches; its potential for provocation has faded, and it has given way to many variations, which have themselves become established, such as disorder-specific (Schweitzer & von Schlippe, 2009) and setting-specific variations (Greve & Keller, 2010; Ruf, 2005; Tatzer & Schubert, 1997).

It is remarkable that, despite all these developments, no exhaustive definition of systemic therapy or systemic practice exists to date. This could be the result of an almost inflationary use of the term "systemic" or of therapy schools (e.g., systemic ones) protecting their commercial interests. It could also be argued that the reputation of systemic approaches – as a method that is particularly easy to learn – has not furthered conceptual precision.

When googling "systemic therapy," one reads that systemic therapy has its roots in family therapy, which focuses primarily on interpersonal relationships: "Systemic therapy […] seeks to address people not on an individual level, as had been done in earlier forms of therapy, but as people in relationships, dealing with the interactions of groups and their interactional patterns and dynamics." (website of the German Society for Systemic Therapy and Family Therapy) On this website a well know German psychotherapist (Wilhelm Rotthaus) refers to the relationship of the individual with his or her social references:

> Mental illnesses are defined as dysfunctions of the system-environment-fit. Individual symptoms are seen as the result of illness-inflicting and illness-maintaining relationship patterns in the context of the patient's loved ones and significant others. The patient's significant others are therefore included in the therapy process whenever possible. (www.dgsf.org)

Furthermore, Rotthaus refers to the "dynamic interdependencies between biological and mental characteristics" on the one hand, and the "social conditions of life" on the other hand, as well as applications other than family therapy; namely, individual therapy and couples counseling.

It is clear that the family therapy setting is an important part of systemic therapy, but it is neither essential nor sufficient for its definition. Family therapy is also present in other therapies that do not share the systemic approach, such as psychoanalysis (Richter, 1962, 1970), behavioral therapy, and psycho-educative approaches (here with broad empirical foundations: Hahlweg & Weidemann, 1999; Hahlweg, Dose, Dürr, & Müller, 2006; Heinrichs, Bodenmann, & Hahlweg, 2008; Sexton, Alexander, & Mease, 2004). The same is true for marriage counseling (Heinrichs et al., 2008; Sexton et al., 2004). The origins of couples counseling and family therapy lie partly in the not-so-recent past (i.e., the establishment of educational and family counseling services by Alfred Adler in the 1920s: Bruder-Bezzel, 1991; Adler Studienausgabe, Vol. 4, Dalter, Gstach, & Wininger, 2009), where Adler in particular adopted a therapy approach that included the family's social networks (for example, schools) as well as their respective economic and societal living conditions (Adler Studienausgabe, Vol. 7, Bruder-Bezzel, 2009) (see Figure 1).

As with any other therapeutic method, it is possible to perform individual therapy with systemic elements, be it by strongly emphasizing the client's family relations (family therapy without the family: Weiss, 1988) or by not explicitly mentioning this reference (i.e., the case in solution-focused approaches: de Shazer, 1985; Walter & Peller, 1992).

Therefore, neither the setting nor the number of people involved can be seen as essential parts of the definition of systemic practice. Conceptually, dynamics of and within the mind can be interpreted as a "mental system" (Ludewig, 2011; Luhmann, 1984). Examples are the intrapsychic dynamics in the person-centered systems approach (Kriz, 1990, 2004) or biopsychosocial approaches that are particularly programmatic in psychosomatic medicine (von Uexküll, Adler, Herrmann, Köhle, Schonecke, & Wesiack, 2011). Even though the relations between social, mental, and biological system levels cannot ultimately be resolved and positions held on this topic in the fields of philosophy of mind and neurophilosophy are often contradictory, in systemic therapy, it would be difficult to justify disregarding mental (psychic) or biological processes.

Figure 1
Alfred Adler (1870–1937). His "individual psychology" was much less individual-centered than the name suggests. This approach clearly places the person in the context of family and other social groups, also in terms of the socioeconomic situation. In the "red Vienna" of the 1920s, Adler established numerous educational counseling centers that explicitly worked with the families and teachers as well as the whole school system of a child experiencing difficulties. ©DGIP-Archiv Gotha.

It would be misguided to define psychotherapy as a primarily language-based process (e.g., Anderson & Goolishian, 1988), since the systemic approach takes several levels of systems functioning into account. In some respects, such an exclusive claim on language could even be seen as reductionist. Reductionism takes a multi-dimensional and complex phenomenon and confines it to one specific or (too) few dimensions. This could be the reduction of emergent phenomena (e.g., life, consciousness, or interpersonal structures) to reputed underlying subsidiary systems or components, which, taken to its extreme, results in materialism or physicalism. In other words, reductionism views the world from a point of view that does not consider the possibilities of other approaches or theories of reality. It leaves no room for the appreciation of tentativeness, the temporal and contextual narrowness of the here and now, nor its necessary dependence on the perspective of everyday as well as scientific observations and descriptions. The same would hold for a systemic theory if it were reduced to the bare components of language and social functioning.

Another way of defining systemic therapy and practice identifies "context" – and the manner in which context is factored into the therapeutic process – as its distinguishing feature. However, if we characterize "context" as the current or biographical relevant social environment of a patient, it soon becomes clear that context plays a role in the majority of therapy methods (albeit with different emphases). Let's imagine a child is having problems at school. It would be difficult to find a therapy that did not consider the parents, teachers, peers, or classroom when addressing the issue. The same is true for other mental health disorders that span an entire lifetime. Of course, there are differences in how these contexts are analyzed and whether the relevant people in the social environment are integrated into the therapy in a virtual or concrete manner. On the other hand, if we characterize context as the environment of a system and its interaction, synchronization, and coupling with other systems, we could argue that context forms part of each and every empirical and/or mathematical systemic analysis (Osipov, Kurths, & Zhou, 2007; Pikovski, Rosenblum, & Kurths, 2001) and is by no means specific to a particular psychotherapeutic school.

It is equally unfruitful to define systemic therapy by its orientation towards the patient's resources and competences, even though this approach – a counter movement to the psychiatric mainstream that oriented itself towards the patient's deficiencies and pathologies – has been prioritized by many therapy methods in recent years. Elements of this approach can be found in Milton Erickson's work, from where the focus on resources entered systemic therapy and counseling via the solution-focused practice of Steve de Shazer and Insoo Kim Berg (Berg & Miller, 1992; de Shazer, 1985; Miller, Hubble, & Duncan, 1996). At this point, it is also worth noting the salutogenesis concept (Antonovsky, 1987) and the empowerment movement within community psychology and psychiatry (Keupp, 1997; Knuf & Seibert, 2009). Klaus Grawe (2004a) made the focus on resources one of the main components of his "general psychotherapy."

Perhaps we could define therapy schools by a countable quantity of therapy and intervention methods. For example, for systemic therapy, one could call to mind circular questions, family, team and other constellations, genogram work, and the use of reflecting teams (for an overview of systemic tools, see Schwing & Fryszer, 2006). However, as new techniques and intervention methods are continually invented, this definition – albeit plausible – is problematic, since it may fail to reflect current developments. Furthermore, most therapy methods also use techniques that were developed within other therapy schools, usually with slight modifications and/or a simple change of label. This point is illuminated perfectly when reflecting on the excessive use of hyphens in names such as systemic-behavioral therapy, hypno-systemic therapy, systemic-psychoanalytic therapy, and so on. The use of just one approach is clearly viewed as too limiting by many practitioners. In fact, most practitioners adopt an eclectic approach, and it is very uncommon to use one "pure" method or therapy school. This fact is paralleled by results of research on factors that influence therapy outcome; this research shows that the therapist's competence and other characteristics of his personality are important factors in achieving a successful therapy outcome (Beutler et al., 2004; Webb, DeRubeis, & Barber, 2010). For competence and personality to be utilized, there has to be a certain freedom of choice with regards to therapy methods, as not every therapist is comfortable with every method and intervention technique. Therapists should be allowed, and even encouraged, to follow their own therapeutic preferences.

Therefore, considering the relatively limited contribution they make to therapy outcome, it is clear that sets of techniques and methods are not a useful basis to define therapeutic schools. Compared to the client and therapist's personality characteristics, the professional relationship and working alliance, and the so-called unspecified variables, interventions only account for a small percentage of the outcome variance of psychotherapy (Ahn & Wampold, 2001; Lambert & Ogles, 2004; Shapiro et al., 1994; Sparks & Duncan, 2010; Wampold, 2001, 2010). Nevertheless, a significant part of psychotherapy research is focused on the evaluation of intervention methods (perhaps we could question how effective it is to allocate so many resources to this research issue).

Some practitioners prefer to characterize their respective approaches by describing the therapeutic attitude it typifies, rather than the techniques it involves, which also supports the idea that techniques themselves are not sufficient to define a therapy school. However, this simply shifts the question to whether an attitude (regardless of how honorable it is) can be necessary and essential for the definition of a therapy approach. This is highly doubtful.

One of the defining traits of systemic practice that is repeatedly mentioned is its foundation in constructivism or second-order cybernetics. Second-order cybernetics takes the observer into account when describing or constructing reality, or, in other words, it considers the conditions for insights and knowledge that a rational subject introduces in the observation or description of facts. Although it is arguably important to consider the observer, this already forms part of all cognitive science and epistemology (as a central subdiscipline of philosophy) and, in psychology, it is also pursued in hermeneutic, phenomenological, and subject-oriented approaches. It is also the case that, in diagnostics, its epistemological, logical, and methodological preconditions have been discussed on more than one occasion (e.g., Pawlik, 1976; Westmeyer, 1972). Therefore, the question of the conditions for insight is not specific to a certain therapy school. Having said this, it is true that systemic approaches tend to rely to a greater extent on a type of second-order cybernetics, rather than first-order cybernetics, i.e., the concrete systemic modeling of the world. The current use of the term "cybernetic" comprises not only control theories, but also general theories of complex systems, systems biology theories, as well as self-organization theories (see the various topics in the periodical *Biological Cybernetics*).

It remains an open question whether psychotherapy approaches should be tied to specific epistemological positions. The authors of this book believe that such ties are undesirable and should not be required. We are of the firm conviction that psychotherapists should not have to specify their epistemic beliefs; especially since it remains (and may continue to remain) undecided whether the visible world is the result of a construction process or whether construction processes are carried out in exactly this real, visible world (see the fully elaborated argument in Haken & Schiepek, 2010, p. 318 ff.). Research on self-organization postulating analogies of pattern recognition and pattern formation in the brain (e.g., Haken, 1990) certainly suggests a constructivist position; however, many great system researchers would not describe themselves as constructivists, especially not radical constructivists. They could appeal to a number of plausible positions; for example, critical rationalism (and its off-shoots) or a model-depended realism. One could even construct the world as completely linear and monocausal – in other words, entirely asystemic – and it would still be constructed (just not in a systemic way). This would not lead to a contradiction.

Whether and how one positions oneself towards such epistemic questions of principle belongs to the realms of philosophical discourse or personal freedom of opinion. However, as we have seen, it is certainly not useful to appeal to these epistemic questions to define a therapeutic approach, and especially not to define an interdisciplinary, forward-facing development in psychotherapy. Moreover, even within constructivist positions, there is a considerable spectrum of variants, e.g., radical constructivism, social constructionism, neurobiological or psychological constructivism (denoting empirical research of how perception and meaning are created by mental and neuronal processes), de-constructivism, or other variations of idealistic theories of cognition.

It is astonishing that – beside all the mentioned and unsufficient components of a possible definition of the systemic approach – the "real existing" systemic psychotherapy school does not refer to the science of complex systems, e.g., synergetics or chaos theory, for conceptualizing itself. As Pincus states:

> The term *"systemic"* continues to be a powerful buzzword used by professional guilds in family therapy… Yet there is almost no mention within the field of family therapy of contemporary systems concepts (i.e., nonlinear dynamic systems approaches) or research involving nonlinear dynamic systems theory or methods. Indeed, the term *"systemic"* is typically treated as equivalent to *"relational"* or to convey a value for diversity within psychotherapy. As such, modern family therapy is paradoxical at its core; it is devoted to its founding within the general systems concepts of the 1960s and 1970s (von Bertalanffy, 1968; also see Davidson, 1983 for a summary of general systems theory) [or Strunk & Schiepek, 2006, for a comparison of different approaches like cybernetics, autopoiesis, or self-organization models, added by the current authors] but is almost completely cut off from the contemporary systems models that have grown from these earlier concepts." (Pincus, 2009, p. 354, italics in original)

This paradox is even more pronounced after systems neuroscience has entered the field, and is far from being perceived by the systemic conviction.

The fact that it is difficult to define systemic therapy using sufficient or even necessary elements suggests that the systemic therapy approach is characterized by a constantly developing "family" (sensu Wittgenstein) of properties. Of course, this is not something unique to systemic therapy, since other approaches would also experience similar definition problems if sufficiently scrutinized; for example, during a panel discussion marking the 40th anniversary of the German Society of Behavioral Therapy, Dietmar Schulte claimed that the only property of behavioral therapy that still binds us today is the striving for an empirical foundation. But it is precisely this empirical foundation that cannot form the distinguishing feature of any therapy school, as many approaches try to use (or at least claim to use) the scientific method.

Chapter 2

The End of Therapeutic Schools

It could be argued that the vague profile of therapeutic schools, their apparent overlaps, as well as the impossibility of defining them with necessary and sufficient conditions are all signs of the disintegration of an era – the era of 20th century therapy schools. Conversely, efforts are being made to integrate therapeutic schools, and the development of a "general psychotherapy" (Grawe, 1995) that incorporates psychological models (Grawe, 2004a) and neuroscience findings (Grawe, 2004b) in the background is simply consequent. For a number of years, the Society for the Exploration of Psychotherapy Integration has published a correspondent journal, *Journal of Psychotherapy Integration*, in which leading researchers in psychotherapy have presented models for a multi-disciplinary or school-independent psychotherapy (e.g., Castonguay & Hill, 2012; Garfield, 1992, 1995; Grawe, 2004a; Mahoney, 1991; Norcross & Goldfried, 1992; Petzold, 2003; Wolfe & Goldfried, 1988). Arguments in favor of this effort are the lack of empirical evidence supporting the – in parts – pre-theoretical concepts of the various school founders that usually place more emphasis on charisma than empiricism. Proponents of this argument also point to the narrowness of the first-generation approaches that are first and foremost affected by the personal experiences of their founders. This contrasts with the essentially interdisciplinary cooperation in psychosocial care and the results of psychotherapy research, which attach more value to common than specific factors (Duncan, Miller, Wampold, & Hubble, 2010).

Similarly, systemic practice faces the challenge of commissioning multi-disciplinary, integrative developments. Paradoxically, in doing so, systemic practice or therapy ceases to be a therapy school and instead becomes an umbrella term for techniques and approaches with explicit systemic research reference. Complex systems theories would then be the meta-theoretical and meta-methodological frame for school-independent psychotherapy and counseling (Haken & Schiepek, 2010; Kriz, 2010; Schiepek, 2009; Schiepek & Perlitz, 2009).

Results of international psychotherapy research that is not dedicated to legitimate individual methods or therapy schools but instead aims to answer questions of effects and effectiveness of psychotherapy in general (see Duncan et al., 2010; Lambert, 2004, 2013) strongly suggest a multi-disciplinary approach. Moreover, the results of this research put the importance of treatment techniques and interventions into perspective and speak against a linear-interventionist understanding of psychotherapy.

2.1   What Do Interventions and Therapeutic Techniques Really Contribute?

Many studies and meta-analyzes show that interventions and therapy techniques only play a minor role in the therapy outcome (Lambert & Ogles, 2004; Wampold, 2010). The extent of their contribution varies across studies; however, when comparing variables that affect therapy outcome, interventions and therapy techniques consistently rank below those connected to the client, the therapist, and their respective relationship. Wampold (2001) reports 8% shared variance of techniques and outcome, while the *differences* between therapy approaches explain only 1% of the variance. Beutler et al. (2004) report correlations between techniques and outcome between .00 and .11, corresponding to an effect size (ES) of .00 to .20. Shapiro et al. (1994) report effects between 0% and a maximum of 15% shared variance (see also Ahn & Wampold, 2001). These statistics appear to correspond to the views of the clients themselves: When asked what it was that they experienced as most helpful in the therapy process, specific activities or therapy techniques were only rarely mentioned. It was other experiences that took priority, for example, the feeling of being understood and accepted, being provided with a safe place to explore one's own feelings, thoughts, and experiences, receiving support during a time of personal crisis, exploring new behaviors and receiving advice (Levitt, Butler, & Hill, 2006; for an overview over additional studies on the client's perspective, see Bohart & Tallman, 2010, p. 93). Studies on the client's experience of significant events or episodes during psychotherapy also made evident that there are quite different perspectives on the same event – seen through the eyes of the client vs. seen through the eyes of the professional (Cummings, Hallberg, Slemon, & Martin, 1992; Timulak, 2010).

However, it would be hasty to conclude that therapy techniques are unnecessary. Even at a minimal level, they help the therapist to structure his or her own work, and the rituals within the techniques convey the feeling that something important is taking place. Rituals provide structure and security, and they require the client to become active and articulate the rationale of the therapy and its principles. The essential aspect is not *what* is performed, but whether the client accepts the procedure, whether he or she sees meaning in it, whether it corresponds to his or her world view and whether it supports the client's active commitment. If all these conditions hold, there is in fact no difference between placebo interventions and therapy techniques, neither in structure nor in outcome (Anderson, Lunnen, & Ogles, 2010; Baskin, Tierney, Minami, & Wampold, 2003).

2.2   Laymen in Psychotherapy

On a similar note, studies show that laymen – people with no expert knowledge or education in psychotherapy – and so-called para-professionals – people who work in health care but have little or no psychotherapy education – produce very good therapy outcomes when acting as a therapist. Meta-analyzes report that their effectiveness is directly comparable to professional psychotherapists (e.g., Gunzelmann, Schiepek, & Reinecker, 1987; Hattie, Sharpley, & Rogers, 1984). Whether this is interpreted as an argument for the importance of naive social competences or other specifications, one thing is certain: Laymen do not have comprehensive knowledge of specific therapy techniques. Furthermore, results on the effects of therapy education and training (e.g., length of education, extent of self-experience) on the therapy outcome (Lambert & Ogles, 2004) are similarly ambiguous. While intuitively very plausible, the role of therapy training has been challenged and proves to be comparatively small (e.g., Anderson, 1999; Anderson, Lunnen, & Ogles, 2010; Beutler et al., 2004).

2.3   The Dodo Bird Effect

A strong case against the organization of psychotherapy into schools is the so-called *Dodo bird effect* ("Everyone has won and all must have prizes", Rosenzweig, 1936). Since Saul Rosenzweig used this concept in the 1930s to question whether it was possible to demonstrate the superiority of any given therapy school, feelings have run high about it. Understandably, anyone who identifies with a particular therapy school or has invested time, effort, and money into obtaining an education in a particular therapy approach or in the legitimation thereof (e.g., in doing randomized controlled trials) disapproves of the Dodo bird effect or in the legitimization of an approach.

Subsequent to prominent meta-analyzes by Luborsky, Singer, and Luborsky (1975), Smith & Glass (1977), or Smith, Glass, and Miller (1980), most statistical overview studies could, irrespective of their increasingly advanced methods, not locate any substantial differences in the effectiveness of different therapy approaches (for an overview, see Wampold, 2001, p. 72 ff.; Wampold, 2010, p. 56 ff.). Of course, there are counter-examples, such as Grawe, Donati, and Bernauer (1994), who do not accept background effects between therapy schools. However, in general, the majority of meta-analyzes speak against the systematic superiority of one approach, even within specific diagnostic conditions (e.g., Ahn & Wampold, 2001; Benish. Imel, & Wampold, 2008; Robinson, Berman, & Neimeyer, 1990; Shapiro & Shapiro, 1982; Wampold, Minami, Baskin, & Tierney, 2002). The same is true for comparisons of different approaches in couples and family counseling (Christensen & Heavey, 1999; Dunn & Schwebel, 1995; Shadish & Baldwin, 2002, 2003; Shadish et al., 1993; Sparks & Duncan, 2010).

An exemplary assessment of the Dodo bird conjecture can be found in the sophisticated meta-analysis by Wampold et al. (1997). The Wampold group examined 277 studies from the years 1970 to 1995, all of which directly compared therapy approaches that were intended to be therapeutically effective (so-called "bona fide therapies" that are not carried out half-heartedly with little prospect of effectiveness as a means of control condition, but as full-fledged therapy approaches with an expected positive outcome). The authors refrained from classifying the different therapy approaches under investigation into therapy schools (not least because of the vague demarcation lines for the classification of methods and therapy techniques in relation to schools), and they used statistics that considered distribution assumptions appropriately (Hedges & Olkin, 1985). When the effect sizes of the coupled comparisons received positive algebraic signs only, there was an average effect size of .20. This is a small effect size (see Wampold, 2001, p. 53) and can be used as an estimate of the upper limit of differential treatment effects. When the effect sizes of the single treatment comparisons were assigned positive and negative algebraic signs at random, the resulting distribution was a random distribution with an average of zero, with most effect sizes having values slightly under zero. This meets the expectations of the Dodo bird effect. In order to refute the hypothesis, a much broader and flatter distribution around zero should have been observed (to avoid ambiguity, even a bimodal distribution), which would have resulted from a significant number of strong effect sizes or effectiveness differences between treatments.

No significant differences resulted when the compared treatments were grouped into similarity categories. Treatments that were very different from each other did not vary more in effectiveness than approaches that were similar to each other. The year of publication, which could be correlated with the quality of the methodology (perhaps newer studies use more elaborate measures and methods), did not effect differences between approaches either.

For the time being, the Dodo bird effect remains a strong reasoning point. In his 2010 review, Bruce Wampold concludes, "Clinical trials comparing two treatments should be discontinued" (p. 71).

2.4   Allegiance to One's Own Approach

Potential differences in the effectiveness of specific approaches are put even further into perspective when considering an important confounding and biasing variable: the allegiance of the researchers and therapists to their respective therapy approaches (e.g., Wampold, 2001, 2010). It is only human that researchers and therapists show attachment to, identification with, and belief in the concepts and methods they use and that they communicate this to their clients in varying degrees of subtlety. In the practical therapeutic setting, this most likely forms part of the authenticity and professional authority of the therapist and conveys confidence and hope to the patients.

Several meta-analyzes have attempted to evaluate the effect sizes of allegiance. Dush, Hirt, and Schroeder (1983) report values between .60 and .70 (referring to different approaches of cognitive therapies), Berman, Miller, and Massman (1985) report an effect size of .65 when comparing cognitive therapy studies with systematic desensitizing, and Robinson, Berman, & Neimeyer (1990), who analyzed depression therapy studies, report an average correlation of .58 between identification with the methods used and the therapy effectiveness, which equates to 34% variance determination. On the other hand, Gaffan, Tsaousis, and Kemp-Wheeler (1995) report that the correlation between allegiance and therapy result disappeared when comparing newer and earlier cognitive therapy studies. With the exception of this study (as summarized by Wampold 2001, p. 168), the effects of the identification with the respective approach reach effect size values of approximately .65. This is much higher than the upper limit of the differential effect size of treatment techniques assessed by meta-analyzes. As mentioned earlier, this limit is approximately .20, which means that methods contribute less to the psychotherapy outcome than allegiance and other components; for example, the quality of the relationship between therapist and client, motivation and other client characteristics, characteristics of the therapist, or the allegiance itself (see reviews of Lambert, 1992; Miller, Duncan, & Hubble, 1997; Orlinsky, Grawe, & Parks,1994; Shapiro et al., 1994; Stiles, Shapiro, & Harper, 1994).

2.5   Sudden Changes

In the past few years, an increasing number of studies have been published that report discontinuous, abrupt changes in clients' progress (the first of these was by Ilardi and Craighead in 1994) (see Figure 2), which are referred to as "early sudden changes" or "sudden gains" (similarly, abrupt negative shifts are called "sudden losses"). Tang and DeRubeis' (1999a) definition of these phenomena calls for (a) a cognizable absolute size, (b) a consid-

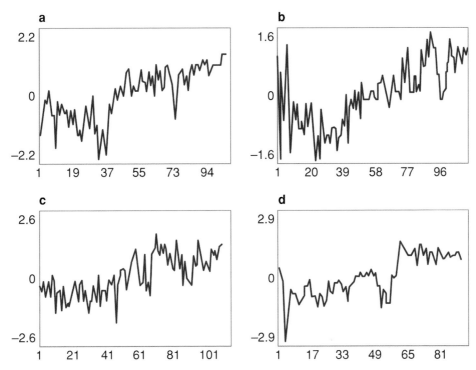

Figure 2
The development of the factor "therapeutic progress/confidence/self-efficacy" of the Therapy Process
Questionnaire (TPQ) (Haken & Schiepek, 2010; Schiepek, Aichhorn, & Strunk, 2012) in four clients.
The TPQ was answered on a daily basis using the Synergetic Navigation System (SNS). (a) Client
diagnosed with recurrent depressive disorder, 101 days of therapy; (b) client diagnosed with obsessive-compulsive disorder, 106 days of therapy; (c) client diagnosed with anxiety disorder, 104 days of
therapy; (d) client diagnosed with recurrent depressive disorder, 86 days of therapy.

erable relative size in regards to the symptoms experienced before the sudden gain, and, (c)
the change to be distinct in relation to the fluctuations in symptom severity before the large
symptom improvement. While these effects were originally observed primarily in depressive
patients (e.g., Busch, Kanter, Landes, & Kohlenberg, 2006; Hayes, Feldman, et al., 2007;
Hayes, Laurenceau, et al., 2007; Ilardi & Craighead, 1994, 1999; Kelly, Roberts, & Ciesla,
2005; Kelly, Cyranowski, & Frank 2007a; Tang & DeRubeis, 1999a, 1999b; Tang, DeRubeis,
Beberman, & Pham, 2005; Tang, DeRubeis, Hollon, Amsterdam, & Shelton, 2007; Vittengl,
Clark, & Jarrett, 2005), it has been demonstrated that sudden changes are in no way specific
to depression, but also occur in other clinical disorders, such as bulimia, alcoholism, and
obsessive-compulsive disorders (Heinzel, Tominschek, & Schiepek, 2014; Schiepek et al.,
2009; Schiepek, Tominschek, & Heinzel, 2014; Stiles et al., 2003; Wilson, 1999).

In a recent study (Schiepek et al., 2009; Schiepek et al., 2013), we identified a temporal
coincidence between an obsessive-compulsive patient's discontinuous reduction in symptoms (measured weekly using the Yale-Brown Obsessive Compulsive Scale [Y-BOCS],
Goodman et al., 1989) and articulate changes in neuronal activity (measured repeatedly
during the therapy process with functional magnetic resonance imaging [fMRI] using an
individualized stimulation paradigm with individual symptom-provocative images contrast-

ed with standardized neutral and disgust-provoking pictures). Strikingly, the most drastic
change in obsessions and compulsive actions, as well as in neuronal activity, took place
before the main intervention (exposure with response prevention) (see also Section 9.3,
Figure 32).

Discontinuous changes can be displayed using a variety of outcome measures and symptom scales. They are neither limited to manualized cognitive therapies nor to the standardized setting of randomized comparative studies (Tang, Luborsky, & Andrusyna, 2002).
Stiles et al. (2003) identified sudden gains in different diagnostic groups and therapy approaches in routine practice, Stulz, Lutz, Leach, Lucock, and Barkham (2007) documented
sudden changes in ambulant daily practice, and Kelly et al. (2005) recorded sudden changes
in group therapy. Spontaneous changes in symptoms can also be seen completely outside
the therapeutic setting and in the absence of any intervention (Kelly, Roberts, & Bottonari,
2007), as in the case of the often-cited *pre-session changes*, which occur between the decision to undergo therapy or counseling and the first therapeutic session or admission to
inpatient treatment (Lawson, 1994; Weiner-Davies, de Shazer, & Gingerich, 1987), and in
quantum changes, which are spontaneous personal changes with or without therapy (Miller
& C'de Baca, 2001).

This is evidently a universal and robust phenomenon that stands in sharp contrast to classical ideas of steady, continuous change (see Figure 3). Discontinuous progress seems
to be the rule, not the exception, and spontaneous, substantial improvements often occur
early in the process and are characteristic of positive long-term development. Several
authors even consider these sudden changes as a necessary condition for therapy success
(Kelly et al., 2005; Stiles et al., 2003; Tang & DeRubeis, 1999a). Nevertheless, the framework of linear input-output models or steady (exponentially damped) dose-effect curves
can hardly explicate this mechanism of action. We are faced with an anomaly of the
classical model; for example, it remains difficult to explain how cognitive reprocessing
can take place without cognitive interventions. Attempts to identify a causal link between
discontinuous change and other relevant, previously occurring changes have not yielded
clear results. Kelly et al. (2005) could not locate significant changes in self-esteem, attribution style, parallel therapies, or medication that occurred prior to sudden gains. It has
been suggested that this phenomenon can be classified as a common factor, such as the
induction of positive expectations, hope, or a good rapport between therapist and client
(Ilardi & Craighead, 1994, 1999). In the next chapter we will design an alternative hypothesis on this phenomenon.

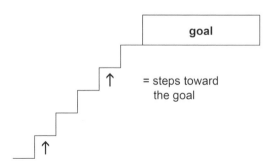

Figure 3
Previous models suggested a linear and continuous therapy progress from an initial problem state to a targeted solution state (adapted
from Reinecker, 1987).

2.6 The Heroic Client

As the title *The Heroic Client* – a book by Duncan, Miller, and Sparks (2004) – states it is the client that has a substantial (if not the main) impact on the therapy outcome. Orlinsky, Ronnestad, and Willutzki (2004, p. 324) identify "the quality of the patient's participation […] as the most important determinant of outcome." In particular, they list cooperation and willingness to cooperate, how the client experiences the relationship to the therapist, the patient's contribution to the quality of this relationship, the adequacy and fit of the client with the therapy approach, the client's emotional expressiveness, the acknowledgement the client gives to the therapist, the emotional and verbal openness of the client, as well as self-relatedness and acceptance of the treatment by the client. In the generic model of Orlinsky et al. (2004, p. 321), interventions have no direct impact on the therapy outcome (neither during nor after the session), because the results essentially depend on the self-relatedness, acceptance, and other psychological processes of the client. Additionally, Grawe (1995, 2004a) highlights the importance of the client's intrinsic motivation as a factor that strongly affects the therapy result. Regardless of how heavy the psychological strain, all pressure from the outside and all extrinsic motivation needs to be transformed into personal intrinsic motivation, goals, and approach gradients in order to become the driving force of the change process.

Asay and Lambert (1999) attribute 40% of the outcome variance to the client and the client's direct social environment. Wampold (2001) identifies that (only) 13% of the therapy outcome is determined by direct therapy factors (therapist, therapy approach and techniques, relationship between client and therapist, allegiance, placebo conditions), which leads Bohart and Tallman (2010, p. 84) to argue that, even if we account for error variance, a major percentage of the outcome variance remains to be accounted for by the client and his/her human eco-system.

Many people can overcome temporary psychological strains by themselves (Gurin, 1990). Lambert, Shapiro, and Bergin (1986) estimate that 40% of all people with diagnosable issues solve these without professional help or interventions. Such a development is called "spontaneous recovery" or – particularly in children and adolescents – "resilience." In these instances, the affected person him-/herself as well as his or her social environment (e.g., people who act as resources and other resources that can be activated), play the essential role. Such persons never adopt the role of a client or patient and they never seek professional help. Even in severe cases or cases of diagnosable chronic mental illnesses (borderline personality disorder, psychosis, addiction, post-traumatic stress disorder), positive changes without professional intervention seem possible (Skodol et al., 2007; Tedeschi & Felson, 1994; Tedeschi, Park, & Calhoun, 1998; Zanarini, Frankenburg, Hennen, Reich, & Silk, 2006). It has also been documented that low-threshold internet-based therapies can be effective (Barak, Hen, Boniel-Nissim, & Shapira, 2008; Bee et al., 2008; Knävelsrud & Maercker, 2007; Lange, van de Ven, Schrieken, & Smit, 2004; Spek et al., 2007) and that positive outcomes can also be achieved by consulting self-help literature (Norcross, 2006). In their meta-analysis of the effects of bibliotherapy, Gregory, Canning, Lee, & Wise (2004) found an effect size of .77, which equates approximately to the effect size of ambulant individual therapy.

One can therefore justifiably interpret psychotherapy as a professionally coached process of self-change (e.g., Bohart & Tallman, 2010; Prochaska, Norcross, & DiClemente, 1994). During professional therapy, there are many opportunities for the client to actively involve him- or herself in the therapy process and display his/her own initiative. Several reviews suggest that the client's perception of the therapy process and the therapeutic relationship as well as the client's creativity, activity, and reflection are crucial for the therapy outcome (e.g., Bohart & Tallman, 2010; Clarkin & Levy, 2004; Garfield, 1994).

It is not only the therapist that coaches the client. The relationship works both ways: The client also coaches the therapist. This is shown particularly by the control mastery theory (Brockmann & Sammet, 2003; Curtis & Silberschatz, 1996; Weiss, 1993), which demonstrates how the client subtly and unconsciously guides the therapist to facilitate corrective experiences and implement scenarios that aid recovery. The client designs situations that suggest a so-called pro-plan intervention; the therapist simply has to recognize this and seize the opportunity. Empirical evidence further strengthens the importance of this point: When analyzing the therapeutic micro-interaction by means of sequential plan analysis (an extension of the hierarchical plan analysis by Grawe and Caspar, e.g., Caspar, 1996), coding the interaction plans of client and therapist in 10-second intervals (Kowalik, Schiepek, Kumpf, Roberts, & Elbert, 1997; Schiepek et al., 1997; Strunk & Schiepek, 2002), we found that therapist and client alternate in directing the process. Using the nonlinear analysis technique Pointwise Conditional Coupling Divergence (PCCD), we established that each interaction partner takes the lead in turn and affects the dynamics of the other person, meaning that the coupling works both ways (Haken & Schiepek, 2010, p. 525 ff.).

2.7   Should We Follow Manuals?

While "allegiance" – how much the therapist identifies with the approach he or she uses – is important, "adherence" – how closely the therapist follows the therapy manual – appears to be of less significance. It seems that neither a therapy process that adheres to a manual nor how closely the therapist follows the manual substantially contributes to a successful therapy outcome, especially not when adherence to manual and therapist competence are distinguished (Beutler et al., 2004; Robinson et al., 1990; Wampold, 2001). As Wampold writes

> The meta-analytic evidence suggests that the use of manuals does not increase the benefits of psychotherapy. In the area of depression, manual-guided treatments do not result in superior outcomes to nonmanualized treatments. Moreover, it appears that treatments administered in clinically representative contexts are not inferior to treatments delivered in strictly controlled clinical trials, where adherence to treatment protocols is expected. (2001, p. 175).

It appears as though the extent to which therapists refer to manuals depends not only on whether they were trained to do so, but also on how much progress their clients make during the first few therapy sessions. In a study by Barber, Crits-Christoph, and Luborsky (1996), improvements in the first three sessions could predict the use of manuals in the next session. The relation between therapy outcome and the use of manuals is thus influenced by the client's compliance and motivation. Perhaps it is also reasonable to assume that the success of a particular therapy strategy will determine how closely the therapist abides by that strategy in the future.

Within the scope of the National Institute for Mental Health (NIMH) depression project, Shaw et al. (1999) showed that competence of the therapist is only predictive of therapy outcome when controlling for the variable "adherence to manual." Could it be that the use of manuals has a potentially damaging effect because it prevents the therapist from displaying his/her competence? If the client–therapist relationship is problematic or the client doubts the selected therapy strategy, then it could indeed be damaging for the therapist to attempt to solve this situation by adhering even more strictly to the therapy rationale and encouraging the client to do the same (Castonguay, Goldfried, Wiser, Raue, & Hayes, 1996). Almost paradoxically, adhering to the concept of a time-limited dynamic therapy (Henry, Schacht, Strupp, Butler, & Binder, 1993a; Henry, Strupp, Butler, Schacht, & Binder, 1993b) affected the quality of this therapy approach in a negative way. This is surprising in so far as this approach was developed specifically to improve the relationship between therapist and client; for instance, by teaching the therapist to avoid angry or hostile reactions when the client exhibits difficult or negative behavior. The therapists who were trained in this way did exactly as they were taught, but to no effect on the therapy outcome: "Attempts at changing or dictating specific therapist behaviors may alter other therapeutic variables in unexpected and even counterproductive ways" (Henry et al., 1993b, p. 438).

From a systemic point of view which emphasizes the nonlinear dynamics and individuality of the complex system "therapy," the use of manuals and standardized procedures conflict with the necessary process orientation and adaptation of the treatment. The ascribed functions of manualized therapies (e.g., justification of and structure in the therapy approach, being able to relate specific treatments to therapy outcome, transparency) can now be accomplished just as well (and, in some cases, even better) by internet-based documentation and process monitoring methods (Lambert, Harmon, Slade, Whipple, & Hawkins, 2005; Lutz, Böhnke, & Köck, 2010; Schiepek & Aichhorn, 2013).

2.8   The Therapist

Despite the success of internet-based therapies, self-help literature, and self-initiated life changes, it is widely accepted that the therapist plays a central role in psychotherapy. The focus here is primarily on the therapist's personality, empathy, experience, social and other competencies, and the genuine, authentic, and honest nature of his or her actions (hence, the old "Rogers variables" of the client-centered therapy), and less on the therapy school or the theoretical ideas to which she/her orientates her-/himself. The latter only plays a marginal role. Wampold (2001, p. 184 ff. and p. 205) estimates the effect size of the therapist variables as between .50 and .60.

When considering the influence the therapist's qualities have on the therapy outcome, it seems as though the therapist has a considerable amount of leeway to shape the therapy process. This refers to choosing the precise therapy technique that not only suits the client and the problem, but also the personality, the personal style, and the preferences of the therapist him-/herself (Miller, 2012). It is imperative that the therapist feels authentic and secure. Furthermore, there is also room to shape the micro processes of the relationship; namely, the way in which the therapist responds to the client's actions and how the patient is actively involved in the therapy process.

2.9   The Therapeutic Relationship

Last but not least, we would like to address *the* topic that runs like a thread through practice and research: the quality of the relationship between client and therapist (Grencavage

& Norcross, 1990; Norcross, 2002, 2010; Norcross & Lambert, 2005). As Wampold writes, "The alliance between the client and the therapist is the most frequently mentioned common factor in the psychotherapy literature" (2001, p. 149). Wolfe and Goldfried (1988, p. 449) call it the "quintessential integrative variable" in psychotherapy. Among others, Horvath and Symonds (1991) and Martin, Garske, & Davis (2000) published meta-analyzes on the correlation between therapeutic relationship and therapy outcome (compare also Crits-Christoph et al., 2011). Wampold estimates the effect size of the "working alliance" as .45. When asked retrospectively to list the factors that contributed to their successful therapy, the clients themselves awarded a prominent position to the relationship they had to their therapist (Elliott & James, 1989; Sloane, Staples, Cristol, Yorkston, & Whipple, 1975). Of all the possible perspectives on the relation between relationship quality and treatment outcome, the client's point of view is the most relevant; in other words, the correlation between outcome and the patient's take on the quality of the relationship to his/her therapist is higher than the correlation between outcome and the therapist's rating of their relationship or third party analysis (e.g., via external rating or video analysis, Horvath & Symonds, 1991; Orlinsky et al., 1994).

According to Norcross (2010, p. 118 ff.), the following factors influence (among other things) the quality of the relationship between client and therapist in a positive way:

- The therapist's empathy (ES = .32; Bohart, Elliott, Greenberg, & Watson, 2002)
- The strength of the working alliance, including the components (a) concordance in therapy goals, (b) accordance in procedure and client's activity, and, (c) emotional attachment
- Positive regard
- Congruence, authenticity, and personal integrity of the therapist
- Appropriate feedback to client behavior and therapy progress
- Repair of alliance ruptures (see Gumz, Brähler, Geyer, & Erices, 2012)
- Therapy goal concordance (ES = .72) and cooperation (ES = .68; Tryon & Winograd, 2011)
- Self-disclosure of the therapist
- How the therapist deals with countertransference
- Quality and adequateness of the interpretation of relationship and interaction phenomena by the therapist
- In group therapy programs: group cohesion

2.10 Psychotherapy as a Complex System

The interaction of the aforementioned variables and components constitutes a complex system that can lead to various, highly individual and idiosyncratic developments. Several authors mention this explicitly, such as Clarkin and Levy (2004, p. 215): "The client variables are in a dynamic and ever changing context of therapist variables and behaviour." However, thus far, we lack precise systemic models to illustrate the interrelation of these factors. We can assume that the interactions between the factors are nonlinear, meaning that there are no proportional and linear (i.e., mathematically represented by a straight line) relations between them. Given this, the estimates of how much variance of the overall therapy outcome a single component explains can only be interpreted as a rough indicator of a greater or lesser importance of single aspects. In some cases, even very small differences in a factor value can have huge consequences; for example, when self-organized thresholds

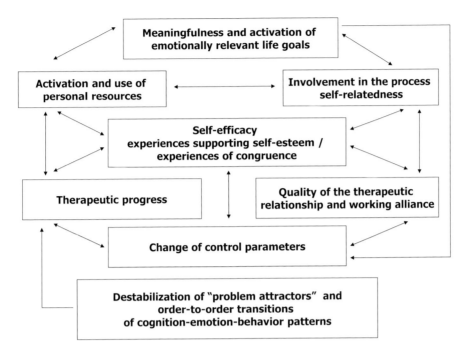

Figure 4
Network model of therapy-relevant constructs. We can suppose that the nonlinear interactions between the variables constitute the individual course of a therapy. However, psychotherapy research has not yet been able to specify these interactions and the parameters that determine them (adapted from Schiepek & Cremers, 2003).

are crossed or changes in dynamic patterns are triggered. Here, components are not additive and the principle of superposition cannot be applied. At this point, it would be appropriate to formulate qualitative models of the interaction of therapy-relevant factors, so that, in a next step, therapy processes can be simulated in computer simulations (Liebovitch, Peluso, Norman, Su, & Gottman, 2011; Peluso, Liebovitch, Gottman, Norman, & Su, 2012).

Figure 4 provides an example of a model of therapy-relevant factors (Schiepek & Cremers, 2003) that was developed in the style of Grawe (1995). It contains the aspects meaningfulness of the therapy for the client; relatedness to his/her vision of life; activation and use of personal resources; quality of the relationship to the therapist; receptiveness towards the therapeutic offerings and interventions; development of experienced congruence (Grawe, 2004b); self-efficacy and self-esteem; and the therapy progress as recognized by the client. The interaction of the factors converges to the control parameter(s) of the system. In the theory of self-organized systems, control parameters are the factors that, when altered, can lead the system to a state of critical instability and to transitions into changed states (Haken & Schiepek, 2010). In many cases, the energetic stimulation of a system is involved, while parameters change the interaction of the factors. This leads to a destabilization of the dynamic pattern (in the therapeutic context, Grawe, 2004a uses the term "problem attractors") and a transition to a new pattern. As humans are beings with integrated cognitions (e.g., perceptions, evaluations, intentions), emotions, and behavior, we use the term "cognition-emotion-behavior pattern" or CEB pattern.

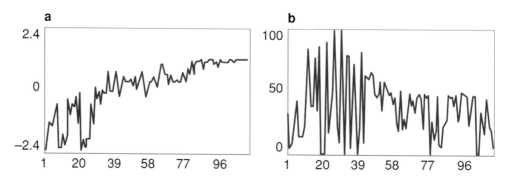

Figure 5
Examples of the changes in dynamical patterns during the therapy process. (a) The changes in the factor "therapeutic progress/confidence/self-efficacy" (z-transformed) of the Therapy Process Questionnaire (TPQ) (Haken & Schiepek, 2010; Schiepek et al., 2012) in a client diagnosed with recurrent depressive disorder. (b) The dynamics of "self-esteem" in a client diagnosed with borderline personality disorder (also taken from the TPQ) is displayed. (a) depicts a change from rhythmical patterns to stable and continuous improvement; (b) shows an order transition from highly frequent (daily) fluctuations to a more stable pattern with less variance and irregular downward fluctuations toward the end.

When therapy-relevant factors are measured regularly, these transitions between dynamic patterns can be identified (see Figure 5). This not only reveals "sudden gains" or "sudden losses" in symptom or problem intensity, but also shows that many of the relevant factors are nonstationary. Nonstationarity signifies qualitative changes in the dynamics of a system, and sudden gains or sudden losses possibly are subtypes of this general instationarity.

Given the conceptual vagueness of systemic therapy, the research results we described in this chapter, and the systemic characteristics of psychotherapy (complexity of the factor interactions and the resulting dynamics), it would only be natural to think of systemic practice in a transdisciplinary and integrative way. In this light, psychotherapy can be seen as a *dynamic and adaptive attempt to provide conditions for self-organized pattern transitions in the biopsychosocial system of the client(s)*. Most processes of self-organization occur in the form of cascades of (for the most part) discontinuous phase transitions – and this equates exactly to "sudden changes." According to this view, professional therapy does not simply perform interventions and techniques based on a pre-structured program, but provides conditions that allow for self-organized restructuring in the client. In Chapter 4, these conditions will be concretized in the form of so-called "generic principles."

A challenge in trying to come to a general form of integrative psychotherapy is for this to not just result in yet another detailed therapy approach. A clear frame and theoretical rigor is required, combined with certain liberties; for instance, with respect to admissible therapy methods. Hence, systemic practice should be eclectic regarding the intervention techniques used within this frame. The therapist should be allowed to choose the method(s) that best match her/his personal competences and resources, but should take into account existing criteria and limitations when justifying her/his choice of procedure.

Chapter 3

Psychotherapy as Providing Conditions for Self-Organization

The above-mentioned requirements of a systemic integrative therapy theory comprise criteria which suggest that a scientific approach using complex systems theory could be promising. It should fulfil certain criteria which can be seen as important challenges in the development of psychotherapy and public health:

- The theoretical frame should ideally be able to explain the results of psychotherapy research detailed in Chapter 2; at a minimum, it should not contradict them.
- The theory should be empirically fruitful; that is, it should generate empirically testable questions and hypotheses that give rise to productive research programs in the fields of psychotherapy, counseling, health care, or clinic management.
- The theoretical framework should be open to the current developments in brain science and applicable to phenomena of neurodynamics, neuronal (re-)organization, and neuronal plasticity. It should make possible the use of brain science in psychotherapy.
- The same is true for psychology and the social sciences: The theory should also have the capacity to construct a biopsychosocial integrative approach for psychotherapy, as already established in psychosomatic medicine (von Uexküll et al., 2011).
- The theoretical framework should furthermore be consistently trans- and interdisciplinary, so that the conceptual and methodological conditions for such cooperation are given.
- The approach should not favor a specific intervention technique or therapy school, but admit methodological variety and substantiate the use of specific methods and procedures in the practical therapy process (adaptive indication).
- The theory should call for process monitoring (including process feedback and evaluation) of therapy and counseling.
- The theory and methods of an integrative approach should accommodate, capture, use, and value the idea that human development processes are individual, manifold, and often chaotic (in a strict sense, i.e., characterized by dynamic and ordered complexity).

3.1   What Is Synergetics?

The systemic nature of our world is the vital basis for most phenomena; in other words, many events in inanimate and animate nature are a result of interactions and networking between parts or components (e.g., atoms, molecules, cells, humans, and so on). Whenever we see mixed feedback – that is a combined positive and negative feedback – and nonlinear interactions – that is, effective interactions between parts or subsystems that are not proportional to each other – the conditions are met that enable patterns and structures to emerge spontaneously. We call this spontaneous pattern emergence *self-organization*. Such self-organization can be spatiotemporal – for example, whirls and convection streams in fluids or the atmosphere, the fur structure of a cheetah, swarm behavior in fishes or birds – but it can just as well be cognitive – for example, the perception of gestalts in a conscious brain (see Figure 6) – or interactive as the cooperation structures between living beings. *Synergetics* is the theory and science of self-organization. It explains how patterns emerge and how they change, how new things come into existence, why some systems are often rigid and stable, and why others (or the same at different times) can change drastically, triggered only by the slightest inner or outer fluctuation. It explores the questions most crucial to therapists and counsellors: How is change possible, what is necessary in order to achieve it, and why on some occasions is it so difficult and on other occasions is it so easy to change human systems, their cognition, behavior, emotions, and communication? In other words: Synergetics provides a meta-theory and a research program to establish an understanding of psychotherapy in general, and the concept of self-organization of complex systems plays a decisive role in this.

Figure 6
Salvador Dalí: Tête Raphaélesque éclatée.
Example of a bistable visual pattern (girl's head
and dome), emerging from a formation of parts.
(© Salvador Dali, Fundació Gala-Salvador Dali/
VG Bild-Kunst, Bonn 2015)

Similar to the autopoiesis concept (similarities and differences are discussed at full length in Strunk & Schiepek, 2006), synergetic theory establishes that, and how, in complex nonlinear systems, it is impossible to influence patterns from the outside in a linear and straightforward way. This leads to the development of a post-interventionist psychotherapy that fundamentally doubts the spirit and purpose of intervention studies (e.g., randomized controlled trials). Psychotherapy can be understood as the provision of conditions for the biological, mental and/or social systems of the client(s) to self-organize; and both client and therapist cooperate on this together. Within the concept of *synergetic process management* (Haken

& Schiepek, 2010; see Chapter 5), these conditions are referred to as *generic principles*. These principles are compatible with conditions for change that are described in different therapy schools and, above all, contain many unspecific factors that have been discussed in psychotherapy research for decades.

Synergetics was founded in the 1960s by the mathematical and theoretical physicist Hermann Haken (born 1927), who initially appealed to a quantum-optical phenomenon – the laser – as an example; the laser light's high coherence results from the self-organizing process that emerges from the interaction of many light-active atoms under certain energizing and boundary conditions (the history of synergetics is described in detail in a recent biography on Hermann Haken: Kröger, 2013). The laser light as order parameter conversely coordinates or enslaves the light-emitting behavior of the atoms, which are part of the system. This means that there is not only an interaction between the particles, but also a bottom-up-top-down circular causality, which creates the emergent functions and/or structures of the system. The bottom-up process (the interaction of the parts creates the order parameter) and, simultaneously, the top-down process (the order parameter(s) synchronize the particles) cooperate. Hence, the behavior of many particles can be described by a single or a few order parameters. This process of "information compression" reduces the complexity of system functioning in such a way that it is sufficient to describe system dynamics at the level of their order parameter dynamics.

This model did not only explain how lasers work, but also became a mathematical formalism (e.g., Haken, 2004) that could be applied to other systems; for example, convection currents and turbulences in fluids or the atmosphere, the emergence of highly complex macro-molecules, or oscillating chemical reactions and auto-waves. It was not even one decade after his fundamental discovery that Hermann Haken and his colleagues began to expand their work to neuronal processes in the brain and the behavior of animals and humans. Early research topics included the spatio-temporal dynamics of epilepsy and motoric coordination (Haken, 1996; Kelso, 1995). The principles of neuronal synchronization and order formation helped to understand fundamental functions and the correspondence between functions and structures of the brain (Singer, 2011). This holds for both the healthy physiological functioning (e.g., of mental resting state dynamics, perception, or brain development; Deco, Jirsa, & McIntosh, 2010, 2013) as well as pathological fields (e.g., epilepsy, Parkinson's disease, essential tremor, and most likely also psychiatric diseases, Tass, 2003; Tass & Hauptmann, 2007; Tass & Popovych, 2012; Tass et al., 2010). Beyond self-organization in the brain (Haken, 2002, 2011) and motoric coordination (Haken, 1996), synergetics was soon put to use in further genuine psychological phenomena, including decision making or perception and pattern recognition (to name but a few; see Haken & Schiepek, 2010). By the 1970s, self-organizing processes in perception were already simulated by the so-called synergetic computer, following the principle "pattern recognition = pattern formation." The emergence and dynamics of psychiatric phenomena and mental problem patterns, the recognition and recall of memory content, and the evolution and experience of the self can be explained in terms of self-organization and be studied empirically (note that the psychological concept "self" is originally not related to the term "self-organization"). By categorizing psychotherapy, group dynamics, and further social-psychological topics (such as the emergence and expansion of attitudes and beliefs in social collectives) as self-organizing processes, a major part of psychology can be described as applied synergetics (Haken & Schiepek, 2010). At this point, it is fascinating to notice the parallels with gestalt psychology, that had already been formulated in the first decades of the 20th century (Stadler & Kruse, 1990).

Human mental achievements (perception, cognition, emotion, behavior) are clearly self-organized, since neither a homunculus nor a central control entity exists in the brain. The dynamic features of complex systems as described in synergetic theory characterize numerous mental and social processes: discontinuous transitions, critical instability preceding phase transitions, nonlinearity, chaotic dynamics limiting the dynamics' predictability, hysteresis involving to a certain degree stable behavior in defiance of changes in the environment, dependency of behavioral changes and learning on control parameters, and the emergence of gestalts and patterns with attributes that are not existent on the level of subsystems or parts (e.g., mental activity in relation to neuronal activity).

Synergetics, as a formal science theory, can be used to create a communication basis for different disciplines. It provides the foundation for new transdisciplinarity that connects not corroborate disciplines like neuroscience and psychology, but also different psychotherapy approaches. In terms of the structuralistic interpretation of theories (nonstatement view; Sneed, 1979; Stegmüller, 1973, 1979; Westmeyer, 1992), synergetics is a formal theory nucleus that allows for intended applications in a large variety of scientific fields when specified and expanded with discipline-specific concepts (Haken & Schiepek, 2010; see the more than 90 volumes of the "Springer Series in Synergetics").

From the outset, synergetics has always been a consistent empirical approach that aims to verify theoretical modeling and mathematical formalization using experiments and data. Within psychotherapy, synergetics has lead to the development of the *synergetic navigation system* (SNS), which facilitates the mapping of change processes and can be applied in routine psychotherapy. By this, process and outcome data are analyzed by nonlinear methods and used for process control and process reflection.

In neuroscience, new technologies of invasive and noninvasive brain stimulation could be developed using the principles of self-organization and neuronal plasticity. The Coordinated Reset® (CR) procedure, for instance, uses the slaving principle of synergetics and reverses it in order to resolve pathological over-synchronization within and between populations of neurons; overly strong synaptic connections are gradually desynchronized (Tass, 2003; Tass & Hauptmann, 2007; Tass & Popovych, 2012). These insights lead to the development of effective therapy methods in Parkinsonian resting tremor and chronic tonal tinnitus. In the future, these methods could also be successfully applied to psychiatric illnesses and combined with psychotherapy.

3.2   How Does Self-Organization Work?

The basic requirement for self-organization is having a system consisting of several elements. This could be molecules in a fluid, neurons in a neuronal network, cognitions and emotions in human mental processes, or the behavior of people interacting in a social system. For self-organization, there needs to be nonlinear interactions between the elements, which is the case in most natural systems. In physical systems – for example, convection currents or the laser – the forces acting on the components can be named and mathematically formalized. Such a system is influenced by external factors (e.g., the supply of energy) or internal factors (e.g., a change in the concentration of neuromodulators in a brain area). These influencing factors are called *control parameters*. They modify the nonlinear interactions between the elements and thereby the intensity and quality of the interaction. This allows for coherent behavior to come into existence across these elements (we speak of

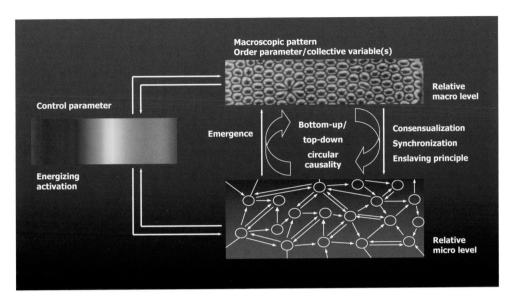

Figure 7
Basic schema of synergetics. Reproduced with permission from Haken, H., & Schiepek, G. (2010),
Synergetik in der Psychologie: Selbstorganisation verstehen und gestalten [Synergetics of psychology:
Understanding and facilitating self-organization] (2nd ed.), p. 134. © Hogrefe.

order parameter(s) or *mode(s))*, or a specific mode can be pushed from its equilibrium and
replaced by another order parameter or order parameter dynamics. Before a mode comes
into existence, different potential forms of realization compete, and one (or several co-existing) order parameter(s) win(s). Before and in phases of *symmetry* (that is, when several order parameters are equiprobable), critical fluctuations determine the realization of a mode.
The mode then enslaves the parts or subsystems (*enslaving principle*), thereby reducing
the degrees of freedom of the system (*information compression*). Hence, there is not only a
causal circular and interactive effect between the different elements, but also between micro
and macro levels. The order parameter (macro level) is a function of the elements (micro
level) and, in their behavior, the elements become a function of the order parameter (circular
causality) (Figure 7).

In physical experiments, the control parameter enters the system from outside in the
form of an energetic stimulation. Examples of this are temperature gradients in fluid layers,
which are achieved by heating from below and cooling from above, giving rise to convection currents (Bénard instability), the light pump in a solid state laser, or a created electrical
voltage in a gas laser. Every system has and needs a specific control parameter; that is, the
system selects the type of stimulation or energy relevant for it. This is demonstrated by the
arrow from the system to the control parameter in Figure 7. It is equally possible that a
system is affected by more than one control parameter, as it is that several order parameters
alternate or co-exist. Multi-stability is the standard case in nonlinear complex systems. In
particular, when the control parameter values change, modes can occur chronologically
(quasi attractors). Every system thus has a spectrum of behavior alternatives available; and
changes in conditions usually do not lead to a collapse of the system, but to its transition
into a new state. When such transitions can be produced experimentally by varying the control parameter(s), this is called a *phase transition*.

In human systems, the situation is usually a little more complicated: We are either unaware of the exact control parameters or they lie in the system's "inside" or they are produced by it, respectively. Another alternative is that the transitions between order parameters and their dynamics occur without systematic manipulation of these parameters. In this case, phase transitions are referred to by the broader term *order transitions*. A transition from a microscopic disordered state to an ordered state is called *disorder to order transition*.

The arrows between control parameter and order parameter in Figure 7 express the fact that macroscopic or phenomenological modeling is possible, even without knowing or explicitly factoring in the micro level, that is, the behavior of the components. The arrow that goes from the order (macroscopic variable) to the control parameter indicates that the system dynamics of some systems can influence the effect, and even the value, of the control parameter. In systems relevant to psychology, this plays a major role, because the system's behavior changes the systems disposition and receptiveness to both external or internal events and, thereby, its parameters. The ever-crucial environmental factors are charted in Figure 8 (the extended version of the diagram in Figure 7).

Micro and macro level are related to each other; that is, the modes or macroscopic variables of one system can be part of a new self-organizing system on the following higher level. This nesting idea of dynamic systems (so-called *nested systems*) looms large in human systems (e.g., neuronal networks in the brain or entities in organizations).

3.3 Neuronal and Mental Self-Organization

In people, unlike in physical experiments, control parameters are often generated and changed *within* the organism. It would be fatal to believe that a counselor or therapist could simply adjust a control parameter and that this alone would effect the desired change. Even when destabilization occurs involuntarily and change in behavior is induced via physical or chemical processes, as in taking psychotropic drugs, the effect is not trivial. Control parameters can affect the neuronal dynamics by acting as antagonists or agonists on neurotransmitter or neuromodulator receptors, but (a) the drugs have to be taken in the first place and (b) their effect depends on other neuro-chemical processes that are, among other things, affected by mental dynamics such as expectations or fears. Chemical substances encroach upon a remarkably complex network (Tretter & Grüsser-Sinopoli, 2011).

In healthy mental functioning, it is primarily sensory stimulation from our physical and social environment, as well as from the inside of our body, to which we react. Therefore, it could be assumed that information functions as a trigger or control parameter; however, information – in terms of "meaning" – is not created until with*in* the organism. Information that cannot be detected by our organism (e.g., radioactivity) is not information for our psychic and mental processes. *Information is generated*, and the initial state of the organism plays a major role in this. Experiences, memories, needs, expectations, and particularly emotions can be seen as system properties that transform sensory input into relevant control parameters. Emotion-related brain structures (e.g., the amygdala) assess the relevance of sensoric stimuli and thereby change arousal, vigilance, and physiological and motoric reactions – and at a pace faster than a complicated cognitive analysis of the situation could be conducted (LeDoux, 2000). Biological systems select their control parameters. Incidentally, this is also true for physical systems; convection currents in fluids, for instance, do not react to electricity or light pumps, but to changes in temperature gradients, and the reverse holds for lasers. Hence, control parameters

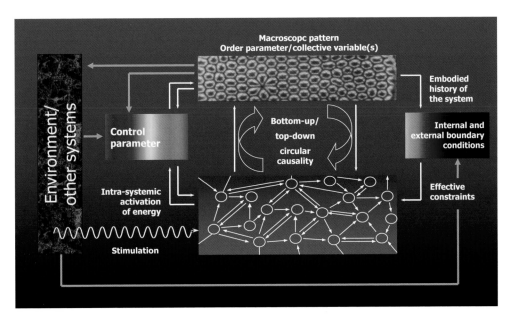

Figure 8
Expansion of the basic synergetics schema (Figure 7) onto neuronal, mental, or social systems.
Reproduced with permission from Haken, H., & Schiepek, G. (2010), *Synergetik in der Psychologie:*
Selbstorganisation verstehen und gestalten [Synergetics of psychology: Understanding and facilitating
self-organization] (2nd ed.),, p. 246. © Hogrefe.

modify the nonlinear interactions between components (e.g., neurons) and remove them from
their momentary equilibrium. There is also a top-down effect on control parameters in neuronal and mental systems; in other words, we are more sensitive to some stimuli than others,
we actively seek certain information or situations and we avoid others.

Processes of self-organization change the behavior, the functioning, and by this the
structure of systems. A system is changed once a mode comes into existence, even after
it has dissolved or merged into new modes. Once established, it is easier for the system
to reconstitute a former existing order (though never in exactly the same way), and each
ordered state changes the probability of occurrence for other co-existing or future ordered
states. The system's history affects the emergence of all further cognition-emotion-behavior patterns and provides the context for the emergence of new patterns and attractors. In
Figure 8, this is referred to as embodied history of the system. On a neuronal level, synaptic
and intracellular processes are modulated function-dependent (second messenger systems,
gene expression). The synchronized activity of the pre- and post-synaptic neuron that modulates synaptic connections is called *spike-timing dependent plasticity* and can be modeled
with mathematical functions (Gerstner, Kempter, van Hemmen, & Wagner, 1996; Markram,
Lübke, Frotscher, & Sakmann, 1997; Tass & Hauptmann, 2007).

Neuronal plasticity is, of course, not random, but influenced by prior formative experiences, especially by experiences in early childhood and/or those of intensive emotional
quality. In Figure 8, this is summarized under *boundary conditions* that constrain the current
system dynamics (constraints). Boundary conditions can be (a) the function of and interaction between the components (e.g., the activability of certain synapses) that manifest in the

system structure (function determines structure and vice versa), (b) the influence of other systems and their order parameters or control parameters, and, (c) physical and material conditions in the environment that influence the system (and vice versa: the organisam can also influence these external conditions, e.g., by selecting or changing them). Therefore, our phylogenetic heritage and the anatomy of our brain can also be interpreted as boundary conditions. As a rule, boundary conditions change more slowly than order parameters, and order parameters change more slowly than single components of a system.

The scheme depicted in Figure 8 can be imagined as connected in multiplex parallel; that is, in hypercycles or hypernetworks of self-organized systems that trigger each other. The dynamics of the order parameters of one system can become a control parameter for another system, and vice versa. The macroscopic dynamic of a system can synchronize with other systems and result in new orders at the next level. A small neuronal network interlinks with other networks in a cluster, which is in turn become part of a bigger cluster-of-clusters, and so forth. The self-organization of a system expands into a hierarchy of systems, and, in doing so, the macroscopic order dynamic of one system becomes the micro process of the next system, and so on. This holds for neuronal, mental, and interpersonal processes.

On a more complex level, behaviors can also be seen as order parameters that influence our environment. We choose which environments we act in (e.g., the people we interact with) and actively shape them. Conversely, we receive signals from the environment. Although "environment" is depicted as an undifferentiated block in Figure 8, it of course also contains self-organizing systems of different types and dimensions, in which we are

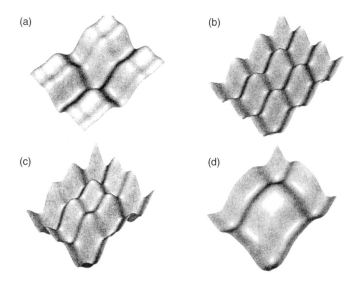

Figure 9
Example of a changing potential landscape. (a) symbolizes the pull of a dominant problem attractor; (d) a repellor has evolved from a dominant order state. The sequence of potential landscapes illustrates the transition from a nearby mono-attractor state (a) into multi-stability (b, c). Multi-stability of evolving potential landscapes is an essential feature of healthy and adaptive functioning in complex systems (Deco et al., 2013) and an enabling mechanism for development and learning. Reproduced with permission from Haken, H., & Schiepek, G. (2010), *Synergetik in der Psychologie: Selbstorganisation verstehen und gestalten* [Synergetics of psychology: Understanding and facilitating self-organization] (2nd ed.), p. 45. © Hogrefe.

integrated and with which we interact. When people observe and evaluate each other in so-cial interactions, we are talking about so-called *endosystems* (Atmanspacher & Dalenoort, 1994). These come into play when phenomena are not just observed, but their creation depends on observers which co-create them. Our ability for reflected introspection and con-tinuous self-monitoring makes us such observers.

The environment of self-organizing systems provides conditions that function as control parameters. The structural conditions and changes in our environment affect us permanent-ly, are of a stimulating nature, and produce approximation and avoidance gradients (see the concept *gradient field* proposed by Lewin, 1963). We live in a vector-gradient field that is not unilateral; our perceptions, needs, and emotions co-create this environment (see Figure 8: arrows from system and order parameters to the control parameters). This expresses what the gestalt psychologist Kurt Lewin meant with his formula B = f(P, E): Behavior (B) is a function (f) of a person (P) and his/her environment (E), and that is the environment as it exists in the perception and experience of that very person. Furthermore, the environment establishes the boundary conditions of our mental functioning and behavior.

Consistent with this line of thinking, a synergetics model can explain how mental struc-tures between self and environment are stabilized. In the long run, cognition-emotion-be-havior (CEB) patterns can emerge that are characteristic for a person and appear more frequently. In the *potential landscape* metaphor (see Figure 9), these are the valleys in a landscape representing our *personality* (see Globus & Arpaia, 1994; Schiepek, 2006). When the valleys are not too deep and the mountains between them not too high, we can switch between CEB patterns as appropriate. The landscape changes as a function of landscape use (experience); in other words, our personality can change and develop. This allows us to understand the double aspect of stability and flexibility that constitutes healthy personali-ties. The ball that is moving around in this landscape (current system behavior) alters the shape of the landscape, though on a much slower time scale than the motion speed of the ball itself.

Chapter 4

Conditions for Support of Self-Organization: The Generic Principles

From the theory of synergetics and the results of psychotherapy research (Chapter 2), conditions for the formation of self-organizational processes can be inferred. These have become generally known as *generic principles*. Schiepek, Eckert, Honermann, & Weihrauch (2001) provide a provisional description, but a more detailed version – to which we refer here – can be found in Haken and Schiepek (2010, p. 436 ff.). In his detailed case studies, Rufer (2012) used the generic principles to explain change processes during psychotherapy. Schiersmann and Thiel (2012), Wahl (2012), and Hein (2012) transferred these to counseling, thereby also interpreting counseling as a process of providing conditions for self-organization in human beings. The generic principles are not a phase model that forces a normative sequence on the dynamics of human development processes, but criteria that are permanently relevant in therapy and counseling, though of different relevance in different process stages.

4.1 Stability Conditions

When order transitions are associated with critical instability and destabilization of attractors, it is first necessary to create stable frame conditions. Even in physical systems, phase transitions – which are provoked by modifications in the relevant control parameters of the system – require relatively stable conditions and mechanisms. If, for example, the distance between the mirrors of a laser apparatus (between which a coherent laser wave should build up) continues to change erratically, no stable light wave could be established. The same is true for configuration and construction of other physical self-organization experiments.

In this light, psychotherapy and other treatments that support self-organized order transitions *destabilize in the context of stability*. Stabilization includes all actions that create certainty about the structure (setting, therapy process, comprehension and subjective transparency of the procedure), the quality of the therapeutic relationship and confidence in the therapist (her/his competence, credibility, emotional stability) and, finally, the support and confidence the client gains from inside (experiencing self-efficacy and self-worth, sense of control and manageability, access to personal resources, experience of congruence towards central life goals and schemata in the beginning of a therapy). Referring to Bowlby's attachment theory, one could say that exploratory behavior needs a haven of safety to which one can retreat (Bowlby, 1973, 1980; Carter, Sue, Lederhendler, & Kirkpatrick, 1997). While this principle is relevant in all human learning and development processes, it is of particular importance in the therapy of posttraumatic stress disorder and borderline personality disorder (Bohus, Schmahl, & Mauchnik, 2011; Flatten, 2011; Reddemann, 2001). The control mastery theory contains the concept of "transference tests," in which the patient tests whether the therapist can provide sufficient safety and understanding to address contentious topics, and whether the professional acts in a way that facilitates the client's unconscious development plan, thereby disconfirming the client's pathological beliefs (Brockmann & Sammet, 2003; Curtis & Silberschatz, 1996; Weiss, 1993).

Recently, internet-based monitoring systems – for example, the synergetic navigation system (SNS; Schiepek & Aichhorn, 2013) – have been used as an effective way to provide stability and structure. Periodic (e.g., daily) self-assessments of therapy-relevant aspects and diary writing (also possible in the SNS) are common rituals that can support mentalizing processes about immediate experiences. In this way, they help to structure experiences, are a constant and integrative part of the day, and provide a connection to the therapist even on days without a therapy session.

4.2   Identification of Relevant System Patterns

It is necessary to determine which system the intended processes of self-organization should relate to (system boarders). There are various methods that can model and analyze the relevant CEB patterns and involved processes. The methods of idiographic system modeling (Schiepek, 1986, 1991; Schiepek, Wegener, Wittig, & Harnischmacher, 1998; see below Section 7.3), the configuration analysis identifying client-specific states of mind (Horowitz, 1987), and the plan analysis (Caspar, 1996; Grawe, Grawe-Gerber, Heininger, Ambühl, & Caspar, 1996; Schiepek et al., 1997) are of particular interest. The case formulation retrieved by these methods provides a frame of reference for the therapy process – not least to assess changes – and provides bases and a reference matrix for potential interventions. Different relationship patterns of a client require the therapist to adapt and form the therapeutic relationship accordingly. In interpersonal systems (e.g., dyads in couples therapy, families, groups, or teams), interpersonal processes can be represented in so-called interaction matrixes (Figure 10). Cierpka (2008) illustrates several options (questionnaires, interviews, and observation-based coding) to measure relationship patterns in families.

4.3   Sense of Significance

The client should perceive his or her personal development processes as meaningful and in congruence with his or her life goals. This is particularly relevant for problematic crisis situations. When the experience of "synergity" (Hansch, 1997), internal coherence, and goal-oriented behavior are more or less absent in a given period of life, it is even more important that the therapeutic process is compatible with the client's life goals (concerning date, goals, idea of man, and therapy rationale). This corresponds to the dimension "meaningfulness" in Antonovsky's "sense of coherence" (Antonovsky, 1987). It is only the most significant and meaningful projects that warrant investment of resources and effort (see the concept of "effort justification" in motivation psychology and dissonance theory, Cooper & Axsom, 1982).

Information exchange   **Support**

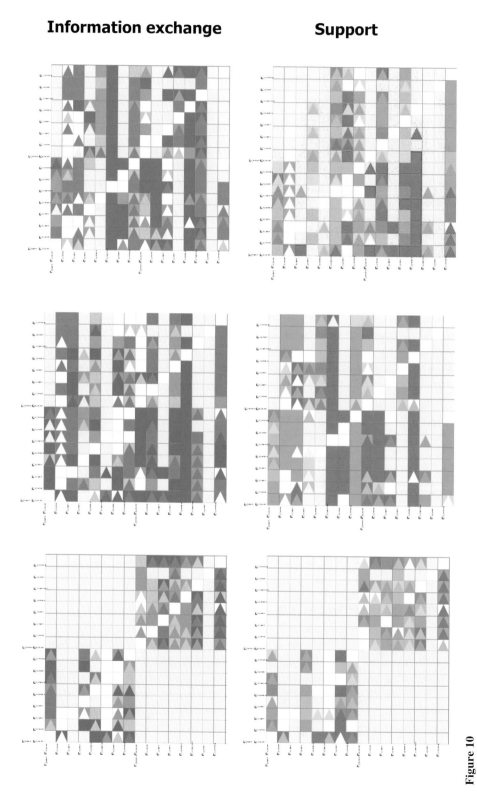

Figure 10

Sequence of interaction matrices corresponding to dimensions "exchange of information" and "support" from a self-rating scale (see also the description in Section 8.1). The interaction patterns were collected during a gaming simulation of a merger of two psychosocial facilities.

4.4   Control Parameters and Motivation for Change

Self-organization requires, in the broadest sense, the energetic activation of a system. In physical systems, there is dissipation that drives the system from its thermodynamic equilibrium. In synergetics theory, control parameters are understood as modulating the interactions between processes and elements, activating the system, and amplifying or reducing system internal inhibition processes (dis-inhibition; Schmid-Schönbein, 1996), respectively. In psychotherapy, we talk analogously about providing motivational conditions, activating resources, and intensifying emotions (Ciompi, 1997), as well as the emotional and motivational significance of goals, wishes, and visions of the client. Unlike physical systems, human systems require not just a direct supply of energy, but a system-internal change of conditions for activation. This can occur through emotional relevance attribution, meaning generation, and by changes in the system-environment interactions. A central concern is always the client's intrinsic motivation for change. Support can be provided by, for example, focusing the therapy goals on the client's personal goals and hopes, or by introducing the so-called miracle question ("What would your day look like if a fairy had been able to solve your problems during last night's sleep?"; de Shazer, 1985; Walter & Peller, 1992).

4.5   Destabilization and Amplification of Fluctuations

Psychotherapy provides the client with new and changed opportunities for experiences. Consequently, existing CEB patterns are destabilized during psychotherapy and incongruences

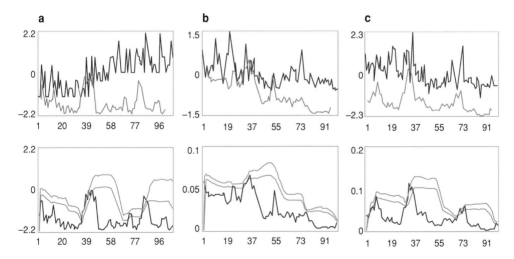

Figure 11
Top row: Evolution of dynamic complexity (red), calculated over a moving window of seven days of the dynamics (dark blue) of the factors (a) "broadening in perspective and innovation" (client diagnosed with obsessive-compulsive disorder), (b) "dysphoric affect", and (c) "discomfort and pressure" (b and c: client diagnosed with recurrent depression). (a), (b), and (c) are factors of the Therapy Process Questionnaire (TPQ) (Haken & Schiepek, 2010; Schiepek et al., 2012). The data stem from daily assessments during 110 (a) and 101 (b, c) days of inpatient therapy, respectively. Bottom row: Evolution of dynamic complexity (dark blue) of (a), (b), and (c) with the associated dynamic confidence intervals of 95% and 99% (light blue).

occur, which, in the beginning, can prove unsettling. Quite often, the client is already prepared for such destabilizations, since he/she has already recognized that existing forms of reality construction, emotional coping, or behavior are no longer adequate. Taking developmental steps forward and dealing with new personal challenges is often intentionally or an unconsciously laden with meaning before destabilization occurs. The client experiences new and emotionally relevant states for an increasing length of time and in increasing degrees of intensity; this is called *deviation amplifying feedback.* In practice, different techniques can be used to interrupt or destabilize existing patterns. These techniques include exercises and role play, behavior experiments, focusing on the exceptions of a problematic pattern, introducing new differentiations, reframing, as well as confronting and provoking methods.

The synergetic navigation system (SNS) makes it possible to take direct readings of critical fluctuations. The algorithm used to calculate them is called *dynamic complexity.* It measures the frequency and amplitude of fluctuations of a time series, as well as the distribution of the values over the respective scale range. In the SNS complexity is calculated in a moving window of freely selectable width, and is displayed as variation in time for each item or factor of a questionnaire. To determine significance, a 95% or 99% confidence interval that refers to the distribution of prior complexity values can be used to define the significance threshold of the current dynamic complexity value (Figure 11; for the algorithm, see Schiepek & Strunk, 2010, and the Appendix of this book).

The Synergetic Navigation System

The SNS makes it possible to directly display the current value of the generic principles 1 (stability and experience of safety, blue), 4 (motivation for change and involvement in the process as equivalent to the control parameter, green), and 5 (gradient of increasing critical instability, red) of a concrete therapy process in a color-coded *traffic light scheme* (Figure 12). A red exclamation mark indicates the further probability that the critical instability could trigger a personal crisis (e.g., relapse, demoralization, psychotic episode). Calculations are based on weighted means (principles 1 and 4) or complexity values (principle 5) of selected items of the Therapy Process Questionnaire (TPQ). While an absolute scale from 0–100% is available for principles 1 and 4, as well as for the additional crisis indicator, is the relative percentage change of dynamic complexity related to the complexity development over the last 7 measurements displayed for principle 5 (when complexity is stable or decreasing, the traffic light display remains white). Saturation of colors marks intensity.

Besides the theoretical orientation on the generic principles, the color-coded traffic light features an individual calibration. This is important, since nonlinear, chaotic systems like psychotherapy realize development trajectories that are difficult to predict, highly individual, and characterized by discontinuities or even by crises (phase-transition-like phenomena). In other words, human development processes are non-ergodic (Molenaar, 2013). Therefore, the SNS, unlike the traffic light in Lambert's system (Lambert, 2010; Lambert et al., 2005), does not act on the assumption of superposition of individual trajectories and standard tracks resulting from averaging over many clients' individual developments. Lambert's system is based on an average standard course of the OQ-45 (Outcome Questionnaire 45) for specific diagnoses and, in contrast to the SNS color-coding scheme, it indicates when the client is "off track," that is, when he/she deviates from an expected standard treatment response. Figure 12 displays the color-coding scheme of the SNS.

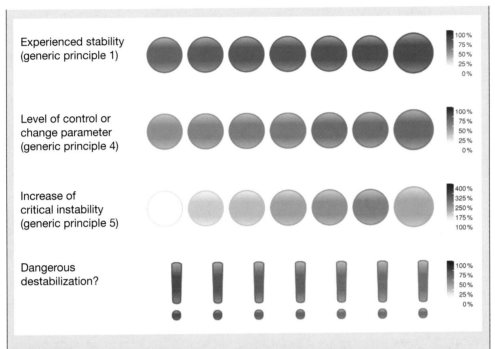

Figure 12
The traffic light of the SNS, indicating the strength of the generic principles 1, 4, and 5 in the actual process of a specific client.

4.6 Cairos, Resonance, and Synchronization

Applied therapeutic heuristics should always match the current cognitive-emotional state of a client. It is unlikely that the client accepts and processes incongruent advice and interventions. The timely fit and coordination of the therapeutic procedure and communication style with the client's mental and physiological processes and rhythms is a condition for and a characteristic of successful therapy. On shorter time scales (in direct conversation during the therapy session), this pertains to aspects like posture, rate of speech, pausing during speech, eye contact, and the use of images, metaphors, and figures of speech. When the client is occupied with emotional processing, it does not make sense to offer new input, unless the therapist purposefully wishes to interrupt the process. Therapeutic heuristics can only take effect when the client is receptive and processes the input in a self-related way (self-relatedness sensu; Orlinsky et al., 1994, 2004). The therapist's interventions should match the patient's current emotional processing depth and quality (Ambühl & Mühlmann, 1991; Sachse, 1992). Therapy questions and therapeutic behavior are interpreted in the context of updated states of mind that accord with respective self and object images and accessible memory content (Beirle & Schiepek, 2002; Horowitz, 1987). When emotional schemata are procedurally activated, completely different experiences are possible and completely different memory structures are accessible than without such emotional involvement (Grawe, 2004a). On longer time scales, this pertains to intervals between therapy sessions or the appropriateness of the intervention to the respective therapy phase. Feelings of success or failure allow for different initiatives and, likewise, action-orientated phases allow for different forms of planning and realization of therapy goals than state-orientated phases (Hartung, 1990).

The term "cairos" denotes this qualified time; that is, the moments that offer certain opportunities and facilitate innovations – for example, within therapy. All that is required is to seize the opportunity. In the systemic concept, these opportunities are the phases of critical destabilization. Gumz, Bauer, & Brähler (2012) demonstrated that, in successful therapies, changes in the dynamic complexity of both the client and the therapist's experience of the therapeutic relationship run parallel and are highly correlated (here, the consecutive therapy sessions were taken as a basis, as opposed to continuous daily assessments of the SNS-based practice).

As a rule, the coupling and synchronization of systems can be viewed as a condition for mutual communication and influence (Osipov et al., 2007; Pikovski et al., 2001; Singer, 2011).

4.7 Purposeful Symmetry Breaking

In synergetics, "symmetry" means that, in a system that is far from equilibrium and close to an instability point or transition-demarkating threshold, two or more attractors or order states are potentially equally likely to be realized. As it is small fluctuations that determine their realization, it is difficult to predict the system's further development. If we invoke our potential landscape image: the ball, the system behavior, is on a separatrix and could roll into different valleys. Neither in psychotherapy can the emerging CEB pattern be predicted or purposefully realized on every occasion; the succession of states of mind is usually left to the process. However, there are situations in which certain CEB patterns should be avoided and not left to chance; for example, because of associated unfavorable patterns of information processing or memory access. Therefore, in order to steer symmetry breakings in a particular direction, certain assistance can be provided; just as sports assistance supports specific movements and prevents others. For example, some structural elements of a new order state can be realized in role-play or by means of motoric exercises. This can cause a certain state to arise coherently and holistically, including the respective emotions: According to the slaving principle, partial neuronal activations trigger more complex neuronal structures, i.e., the full attractor.

In particular, purposeful state realizations make use of human intentionality and the human ability for anticipation. In practice, this is achieved by imaging goal states or cognitively anticipating behavior. Here, the development and mental (preferably also somato-sensoric) representation of goals (e.g., when vividly shaping the answer to the "miracle question") in therapy becomes significant. Similar to an athlete immediately prior to a competition, the client can tune her-/himself into an intended process gestalt (Leist, 1999). At the interface of the approach and avoidance gradient, she/he can kick her-/himself in a targeted manner.

4.8 Stabilization of New Patterns

In psychotherapy, we usually experience not only one but whole cascades of order transitions. Once positive or otherwise therapeutically important CEB patterns are established, they have to be stabilized, automatized, and kept available. Here, techniques for stabilization and generalization of patterns come in; for example, repetition, variation, application in different situations and contexts, or positive reinforcement. Finally, the new patterns have to be integrated in the existent sense of self and linked to present emotional self-schemata.

These generic principles serve to organize and justify the choice of therapy techniques and methods in particular (see the concept "relative rational justification" of therapy decisions; Westmeyer, 1984). Therapy techniques can be evaluated by whether they are able to help realize one or several of the generic principles. It is assumed that several methods or techniques are equally functional in this regard, so that the therapist can freely choose according to his experience, personal preference, and style, thereby maximizing the benefit. The intention is not to normalize the variety of styles and practice forms, but to use the principles to:

- facilitate the theoretical foundation of the practical doing,
- achieve a process-adequate organization of the therapy process, and
- reduce the complexity in practice by evaluating a huge variety of situations with a few criteria.

The relationship between methods and techniques on the one hand and generic principles on the other hand is doubly ambiguous: One method can implement several principles, and one principle can be realized by several practice methods. For example, the principle of energetization (activation of change parameters) can be realized by clarifying goals (e.g., via the miracle question), by activating resources, by factoring in personal cognitive-affective reference systems, or by enabling a first sense of achievement.

Methods and techniques can be compared to melodical and rhythmical sets in the overall process improvization, which are built into the therapy process in a meaningful way: dynamic components of a more complex process gestalt. Generic principles and their theoretical frameworks function as instruments for understanding and shaping, which should allow the therapist to influence the game as participating player, to have an overview, and to motivate and analyze the treatment process. How the process is *shaped* is at the heart of the therapeutic art and expertise. The generic principles facilitate the design, understanding, safety, and flexibility of this process, but they do not replace experience, intuition, and competencies in complexity management. Figure 13 displays the rationale and reference

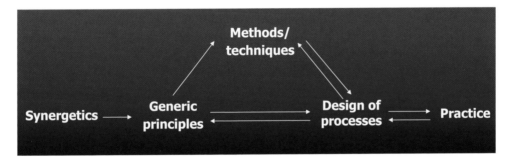

Figure 13
The generic principles of self-organizing processes can help organize, simplify, and justify therapy decisions. They can be used as a guide for deciding upon the next steps in the therapy process. Reproduced with permission from Haken, H., & Schiepek, G. (2010), *Synergetik in der Psychologie: Selbstorganisation verstehen und gestalten* [Synergetics of psychology: Understanding and facilitating self-organization] (2nd ed.), p. 441. © Hogrefe.

connections between the aforementioned aspects of the theory-practice bridging. Table 1 shows how the generic principles can be implemented practically.

Table 1
The generic principles as reflection and decision-making tools in therapy practice

1 Conditions for stability	• Does the client experience the setting as supportive? • Is the therapy process structured? • Does the client understand the process (e.g., the scheduling of emotion-focused interventions) and experience it as transparent? • Does the client have a good relationship to the therapist and trust the therapist (competence, authenticity, emotional stability, relationship tests)? • Can the client receive support and security from within him-/herself (experiencing self-efficacy, control and manageability, access to personal resources, support of self-esteem and self-worth, experiencing congruency with central plans and schemata)? • Are there people who can provide resources in the patient's social environment, support his development process, and offer him/her security and stability?
2 Identification of patterns in the relevant system	• Once we have indentified the self-organizing processes that should be encouraged, we need to establish which system and CEB patterns they refer to. Proposed methods: e.g., idiographic system modeling, plan and schema analysis, resources interview. The case formulation is the frame of reference for therapeutic action and provides information where to place and focus interventions.
3 Meaningfulness/ sense of significance	• Does the client experience her/his development processes as meaningful? • Do the development processes correspond with central life concepts (What is the client proud of? What has been important in her/his life so far?)? • Is the change process compatible with the client's life plan (e.g., regarding timing, goals, rational, idea of humanity)? • Does the client experience congruence in her/his life concerning central needs (approach/avoidance goals; control, understanding, and knowability; attachment and social belonging; self-worth boost, see Grawe, 2004b)? • Can central plans and approach goals be realized?
4 Motivation and change parameters	• Which therapy conditions promote motivation? • Activation of and access to resources (e.g., via resources interview) • Approach goals (what makes the eyes shine) vs. avoidance goals

Table 1. (continued)

	• Intensification of emotions • Emotional and motivational significance of the client's goals, wishes, and visions
5 Destabilization/ amplification of fluctuations	• Are incongruencies experienced? Broach the issue; make them emotionally perceptible! • Are destabilizations of existing patterns already mentally prepared (e.g., does the client feel that the forms of reality construction, emotional processing, or behavior with which he/she has thus far operated are no longer suitable)? • Is the client increasingly often in various states associated with new or emotionally relevant experiences? • Could it be useful to perform exercises, role play, or behavioral experiments, or to focus on the exceptions of a problem pattern, to introduce differentiations or changed contexts of understanding, that, until now, were not utilized, to develop alternative understandings of connections and interpretations (reframing), to use confrontative or provocative procedures?
6 Cairos, resonance, and synchronization	• What state of mind is the client in? • Do the current therapy methods and offers correspond to the current cognitive-emotional state of the client? • Can posture, rate of speech, pausing during speech, eye contact, and the use of images, metaphors or figures of speech be recognized? • Give the client time for internal searches and emotional processing! • Does the client signal receptiveness and acceptance of contents, procedure, etc.? ("Yes-Set" by Berg & Miller, 1992; de Shazer, 1985) • Are the intervals between sessions and the number of interventions adequate?
7 Purposeful symmetry breaking	• Support and assistance: Structural elements of a new order state can be realized by, for example, role-play or by means of motoric exercises. Through this, a certain state can occur coherently for the first time. Matching emotions trigger the activation of CEB patterns. • Imagination of goal states; anticipation of behavior. • Can aids such as symbols, rituals, or resolutions act as anchors in the preparation for new situations and changed behavior? • "Anchors" and small "transition objects" can be taken along in situations where a new CEB pattern has to be established for the first time.
8 Re-stabilization	• Repetition, variation, application of the new behavior in different situations and contexts, positive reinforcement. Integration in the existent sense of self.

Chapter 5

Synergetic Process Management

The concept of *synergetic process management* (SPM) contains a proposal for how psychotherapy and counseling can be designed as supporting processes of self-organization in biological, mental, and/or social systems. At the same time, SPM is also proposed as a concept for an integrative and comprehensive psychotherapy (Figure 14).

The theory of synergetics as well as the mathematical formalism of complex systems theory, which synergetics refers to and uses, are the core starting points of SPM. To pro-

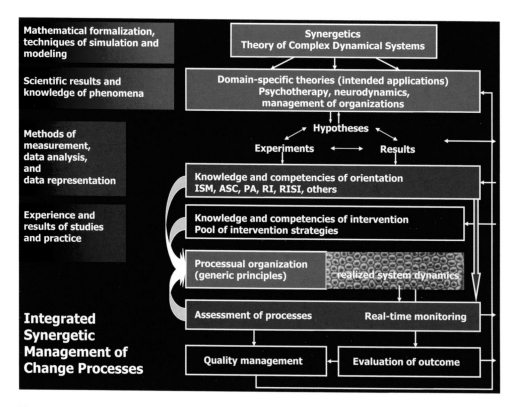

Figure 14

Structure and components of SPM applied to psychotherapy. ISM: idiographic systems modeling; ASC: assessment of dynamical stability and complexity; PA: plan analysis; RI: resources interview; RISI: rating inventory for solution-focused interventions. Reproduced with permission from Haken, H., & Schiepek, G. (2010), *Synergetik in der Psychologie: Selbstorganisation verstehen und gestalten* [Synergetics of psychology: Understanding and facilitating self-organization] (2nd ed.), p. 442. © Hogrefe.

duce concrete specifications of the formal theory core for specific applications, additional assumptions and phenomena-specific relations need to be added. Only such an expansion of the abstract theory core can lead to empirically testable theories for intended applications, e.g., psychotherapeutical processes of change or the dynamics of neuronal systems (for the structuralistic theory concept – also called nonstatement view – see Haken & Schiepek, 2010, p. 277 ff.; Stegmüller, 1973, 1979; Westmeyer, 1992). For this reason, access to phenomena-specific knowledge is necessary.

In a scientific context, this phenomena-specific core expansion makes it possible to derive hypotheses, which can be operationalized and tested with appropriate measurement methods. The methodical spectrum of linear and nonlinear time series analysis is a necessary instrument for the preparation, presentation, and analysis of measurement results, which are usually available as time series collected by real-time monitoring.

Within SPM, a number of methods are used that allow for the presentation of function and network structures of the systems of interest. In Figure 14, these are summarized under the therapist's orientation knowledge and competence. Examples of these methods are idiographic system modeling (ISM; Schiepek, 1986, 1991; Schiepek et al., 1998), methods of plan and schema analysis (PA; Caspar, 1996; Grawe et al., 1996), configuration analysis (identification of states of mind; Horowitz, 1987), methods of incongruency analysis (Grawe, 2004a; Grosse Holtforth & Grawe, 2004), or the resources interview (Schiepek & Cremers, 2003). Cierpka's (2008) handbook provides an overview of the methods that capture interaction patterns in couples and families. These methods serve to identify and describe CEB patterns of clients, both in their social environment and more specifically in their interaction with the therapist. For the case formulation, it is essential to be clear on the boundaries of the observed system that is to be changed, the extension and spatio-temporal resolution of the model, and the observed system level(s) (biological, mental, social-interaction level).

A crucial aspect of orientation competence is to receive information about the dynamic characteristics of self-organizing processes. Process measurement with real-time monitoring methods (e.g., the synergetic navigation system, SNS) offers several possibilities for this, e.g., illustration of item dynamics (time series of raw data and aggregated dynamics of the subscales) and analysis of the dynamic fluctuation intensity and complexity of time series. The degree of system coherence or synchronization (averaged item intercorrelation) during a system's development can also be displayed, as well as continuously changing correlation matrices that document current subsystem and item couplings. These analysis tools serve to diagnose stability and coherence (assessment of dynamical stability and complexity, ASC) in a dynamic system. The measuring sensor of the therapy process's dynamics need not be limited to the client's subjective assessment, which can be performed, for example, by using the therapy process questionnaire (Haken & Schiepek, 2010, p. 363 ff.; Schiepek et al., 2012). In principle, any other information (e.g., from the therapist or from the client's social environment) or physiological data (Fahrenberg & Myrtek, 1996; Fahrenberg, Myrtek, Pawlik, & Perrez, 2007) can likewise be measured and analyzed. Internet-based real-time monitoring systems are at the core of SPM, since they facilitate a data-based navigation through the turbulences of self-organizing developmental processes of a system.

It goes without saying that therapists should have a repertoire of intervention and therapy techniques at their disposal (acquired during their academic education and professional training). Since the therapist is able to consult the experiences and results of different therapy schools and is also able to factor in her/his own preferences, competency profile, and personal style, SPM can, on the level of intervention methods (and only on this level), be called eclectic.

Intervention techniques serve to implement the generic principles and, related to these principles, the functional equivalence of multiple techniques provides the practitioner with space and freedom of choice to realize each principle exactly as he/she wishes. However, we should be aware that therapy techniques are often invented and used within a context of certain beliefs and explanation models that might not be adopted or changed in SPM.

This freedom of choice regarding techniques places SPM in a position that is independent of therapy schools, without having to forgo valuable experiences and findings regarding the effects of different therapy methods that are on hand within certain schools. At the same time, this "middle level" of techniques and intervention methods allows practitioners to retain their identification with their approaches. The independence of SPM from classical therapy schools is also based on the fact that synergetics – a general theory of change and innovation processes – is deposited on a much more general and abstract level than traditional psychotherapy theories. This theoretical frame is the "upper level" (top) of evidence-based practice, whereas the "basic level" (bottom) is the data-based monitoring of the individual process.

Against the background of the generic principles the available information and possibilities for interventions are reflected and analyzed in order to make a client-appropriate therapy choice; that is, one that is suitable for the client's current development and status. The generic principles serve hereby as a filter and criteria for continuous, adaptive indication decisions. The background provides the model of the "relative rational justification" of therapy decisions (Westmeyer, 1979, 1997). In Figure 14, the filter and screening function of the generic principles is symbolized by the arrows that point to the generic principles from real-time monitoring, the clinical-diagnostic modeling of the system (orientation knowledge on the basis of applied assessments; case formulation), and the accessible pool of intervention methods.

Through regular SNS-based therapy sessions, the client is actively involved in process feedback and analysis (see Figure 15). This leads to a cooperative partnership in which the

Figure 15
SNS-based therapy session.

client designs and controls the process to an increasingly large extent. This should benefit therapy motivation, self-efficacy and self-esteem, as well as the therapeutic relationship. And, in fact, these effects are the focus of empirical investigation.

The SNS-based process documentation and analysis include therapy evaluation. It is possible to present questionnaires and to collect therapy-related data at any time (e.g., during initial contact prior to therapy start, at first presentation, at therapy end, as well as during follow-ups). The evaluation results can be integrated into a clinic's quality management and become the basis for the optimization of processes and structure quality.

The SNS provides a complete record of the process and outcome of every single therapy; while single case data can be aggregated and summarized into group statistics. This makes ecologically valid process-outcome research in a practice setting possible. The results and experiences can influence several components and levels of the model and, therefore, can be used to further improve therapy practice and to answer empirical research questions (see feedback arrows in Figure 14).

Chapter 6

The Synergetic Navigation System (SNS)

The trial and development of the synergetic navigation system (SNS) corresponds to the trend to enable ambulatory assessment in the field. Internet-based devices and data collection have led to the application of information technology to new fields, such as psychotherapy, psychosomatic medicine, psychiatry, as well as coaching and counseling.

6.1 Ambulatory Assessment and Real-Time Monitoring in Psychotherapy

An advantage of such ambulatory assessments is their higher level of validity – particularly their ecological validity – and reliability than that of data collection in more artificial situations or the laboratory (Ebner-Priemer & Trull, 2009; Fahrenberg et al., 2007). When the objective is to measure behavior and experiences in everyday life, there is no alternative to using electronic media, especially input devices (cell phones, tablet PCs) with online capabilities (Ebner-Priemer & Bohus, 2008).

The measurement of process data in psychotherapy is one variant of the trend to perform ambulatory assessments. Such process data, usually resulting from the client's self-assessments, can be used to provide timely feedback about the actual therapy process. Lambert and colleagues, for example, were able to demonstrate that process data makes it possible to identify emerging deteriorations at an early stage (Lambert et al., 2001). Although even experienced therapists were seemingly unable to identify such deteriorations, they could be identified by repeatedly applying an outcome questionnaire (Outcome Questionnaire 45; this questionnaire is also available in the SNS). The questionnaire measures the patient's current symptom pressure and functional impairment and thereby enables the identification of therapies that are "not on track"; in other words, therapies that lie outside the confidence interval of reference therapies (averaged processes of patients with similar diagnosis and impairments; Lambert et al., 2002, 2005). At moments when such deteriorations were identified, specific instructions to the therapist contributed to a course correction (Lambert et al., 2005). Further effects of tight process measurement are insights into dynamic patterns, such as the sudden gains or sudden losses in the psychotherapy process outlined in Section 2.5 – such insights would be virtually impossible without the corresponding information technology. Considering the enablement of process feedback and reflection together with the client, the call for a routine use of electronic process monitoring systems in therapy practice (Lambert, 2010; Lutz et al.,

2010; Schiepek, Zellweger, Kronberger, Aichhorn, & Leeb, 2011) is understandable.

At this point, it is necessary to make a fundamental decision about the measuring frequency or sampling rate. If our aim is not only to acquire random status samples, but to identify process patterns, it is essential to perform frequent, continuous measurements. Establishing what counts as a sufficient level of frequent measurement depends on the phenomena of interest and their genuine dynamics (eigendynamics). In real-time neurofeedback with EEG (Rief & Birbaumer, 2006) and real-time functional magnetic resonance imaging (Johnston, Boehm, Healy, Goebel, & Linden, 2010; Mathiak & Weisskopf, 2011), feedback is possible within seconds (even faster using EEG). By videoing the therapy session, the therapeutic communication and relationship dynamics can be assessed with a frequency of every few seconds (Schiepek et al., 1997), though coding the recordings often requires considerable effort, so this method is usually reserved for basic research. When trying to record dynamics and rhythms in circadial areas (e.g., hormone and mood cycles), hourly measurements would be appropriate.

It is not only important to perform frequent measurements, but also consistent and equidistant measurements (regular time sampling). It is only in this way that analyzes in the frequency domain (e.g., fast Fourier transformation, time-frequency distributions; Cohen, 1989) and other (particularly nonlinear) analyses can be conducted in a meaningful way. The following thought experiment illustrates how crucial the relation between the momentum of the phenomenon of interest (eigendynamics) and the sampling rate is: In a completely dark room, a disk is spinning. The disk has a dot painted on it. The dot's position can be determined using a stroboscopic light. Depending on how frequently the light flickers, the dot's position, and thus the rotational speed of the disk, appears to be very different. If the light matches the disk's rotation frequency exactly, the disk appears to be static; however, depending on the light flickering frequency, the disk and dot can just as well appear to be moving quickly, slowly, backwards, or completely erratically. When the dynamics of the phenomenon to be researched is unknown and neither regularity nor information about the measurement frequency is available, it is not possible to provide a sensible account of the dynamics. But this is exactly the situation when psychotherapy processes are measured in irregular intervals (e.g., during the therapy sessions that take place in loose intervals or when taking measurements at several unspecified points in time); and often these measurement intervals vary from study to study, without this being documented. In the future, there should be just as much emphasis placed on standardizing the frequency of measurement as there is currently on standardizing the instruments used for measurement (e.g., questionnaires). The intention is to facilitate an accurate comparison of process research results in psychotherapy.

When aiming at (a) a complete recording of therapies and not just a randomized time sampling of measurements, (b) frequent and (c) continuous measurements, and, (d) having to consider practicalities and the effort that has to be put into data collection, all experience thus far points to *daily measurements*. Experiences at several clinics show that this is feasible. Daily self-assessments in both in- and outpatient psychotherapy are performed routinely using the Therapy Process Questionnaire. This questionnaire, in its current version, assigns 23 items to 5 subscales based on a current exploratory and confirmatory factor analysis using $N = 149$ therapy processes (Schiepek et al., 2012):

I   Therapeutic improvements and degree of goal attainment

II   Symptom severity, strain, and discomfort

III Quality of the therapeutic relationship and trust in the therapist

IV Dysphoric affectivity
V Ward atmosphere and relationship to fellow patients

A former version already implemented in the SNS for inpatient use has 42 items, distributed on seven subscales. An additional version for outpatient therapy uses 47 items.

While classical test theory tends to favor a "true" value that, together with measurement error, constitutes the measured value, process research should attempt to think more in terms of a "true process pattern," subjoined by "noise" or measurement error. What constitutes a true process pattern depends essentially on the constructs used to describe the processes and how they are operationalized, on the system level of observation (cognition, emotion, behavior, physiology), on the measurement frequency or sampling rate, and on the theoretical conception of the process. In other words, there is no such thing as a true process pattern per se, but, as a minimum, it is a function of the aforementioned aspects.

6.2   Functionalities of the SNS

The SNS is a *generic* system that makes it possible to implement various questionnaires as well as rating and observation systems (of course, within licensing laws). It is available for the international market and, since it is generic, all kinds of questionnaires can be introduced, not just licensed ones. Data can be entered using most web-compatible devices, including PCs, notebooks, and iPhones, which procures maximal spacial and temporal flexibility for entering data in the field and ubiquitous computing. Data privacy protection and data security are guaranteed (the security technology is the same as that used during online banking transactions; https pages and anonymized usernames and passwords are used).

Alongside an administrative mode (including user entry, overview of current users as well as an archive for closed cases, granting of access rights, assigning of questionnaires to single users or user categories) and the client documentation, a range of questionnaires can be selected, for example, to evaluate syndromes, severity of diseases and symptoms, satisfaction with the therapy, or attachment patterns. For instance: Depression Anxiety Stress Scales (DASS 21; Antony, Bieling, Cox, Enns, & Swinson, 1998; Lovibond & Lovibond, 1995; Newnham, Hooke, & Page, 2010), ICD-10 Symptom Rating (ICD-10-SR; Tritt et al., 2007), Outcome Questionnaire (OQ; Lambert et al., 2002 , 2004), Borderline Symptom List (BSL; Bohus et al., 2009), BSS (Schepank, 1995), Yale-Brown Obsessive Compulsive Scale (Y-BOCS; Goodman et al., 1989). For process recordings with daily data entry, different versions of the Therapy Process Questionnaire are available (Haken & Schiepek, 2010; Schiepek et al., 2012; translation and norming for english-speaking countries are in progress).

Using the questionnaire editor, personal process recording questionnaires can be created. In order to do this, items have to be formulated, the type and characteristics of the answer scales have to be defined (e.g., Likert scales, visual analog scales [VAS]), and items have to be allocated to the respective subscales. This way, fitted content (e.g., therapy goals, conflict topics, resources) that is specific to single clients, groups, or teams can be gathered (see Section 7.3. below).

It is necessary to define the time schedules of the various questionnaires. Available options are single survey presentation, pre-post tests, time samplings in almost any frequency (e.g., daily), as well as event sampling (i.e., the questionnaire is available again as soon as it is filled out).

In the default option, items are presented in random sequence, but randomization can also be withdrawn. At the end, a comment field appears, which can be used to write a therapy diary or other comments. Questionnaires that were not completed within the allotted time frame can be appended within an agreed time period. In case of missing data, the missing value in a time series is estimated and restored by a cubic spline (i.e., 3rd order polynome). Values that are added this way are color coded in the time series.

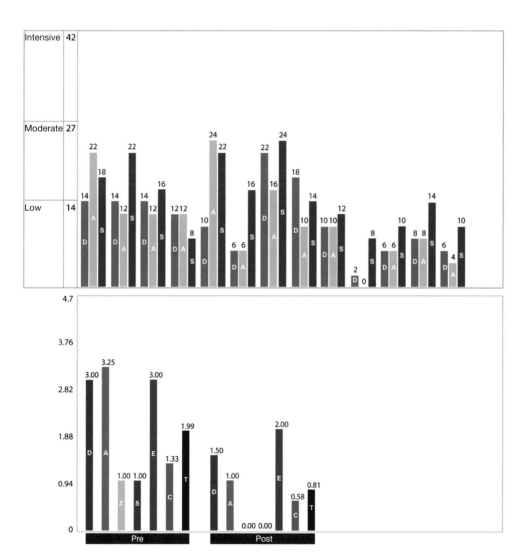

Figure 16

Top row: Evolution of therapy outcome measures (short version of the DASS 21 with 21 items; Lovibond & Lovibond, 1995) with the subscales depression (D), anxiety (A), and stress (S) recorded weekly. The values refer to the case study in Chapter 7 (Ms. B.). The increased values at about mid-therapy correspond to the critical instabilities shown in Figures 17, 18, 23, and 24. Bottom row: ICD-10-based symptom rating (ISR, Tritt et al., 2007) with the subscales D (depression), A (anxiety), Z (obsessive-compulsive disorder [in German: Zwangsstörung]), S (somatoform disorder), E (eating disorder), and C (additional scale) (T represents the average over all scales [total]) at the beginning of the therapy (pre) and after end of therapy (post).

The results of outcome questionnaires are visualized using histograms (Figure 16). The results of process questionnaires are visualized using time series graphs (see, for example, Figure 5, or Figures 21, 22, 23, and 24), where different sizes and alignments of the diagrams can be chosen. The diagram fields can be configured independently, so that it is possible to chart either some or all item evolutions of one client or to chart one item in its evolution over different clients. The selected item configuration can be saved. When activated again subsequently, it automatically loads and shows the current stage of development. When the cursor is moved over the graph of a time series, it displays the value, entry date, and diary entry (the comment field entry can also be made invisible) for each data point.

Averaging and z-transformations make it possible to analyze and visualize the time series of the subscales/factors. Due to the z-transformation, these oscillate around an average of 0 and are displayed in standard deviation units. In a diagram, up to seven time series can be displayed using different colors; it is also possible to chart time series of analysis results. The graphs are optically adapted and calibrated to do justice to the fact that the raw values of the time series (for instance 7- or 100-level resolution), the factor graphs, as well as the analysis results (dynamic complexity, permutation entropy) lie on different scale ranges and resolutions (e.g., see Figure 11). If desired, different time series (e.g., changes in raw values or complexities) can also be averaged.

Above, we have already described the option to depict the current status of three of the generic principles in a color coded (traffic light) format (see Section 4.5., Figure 12).

All generated graphs, as well as the diary entries, can be printed. Furthermore, there is a data export function that makes it possible to export data (time series of raw values, factors or subscales, complexities, and permutation entropy) to Microsoft Excel or csv files. In this way, data can be transferred to other statistics and time series analysis tools. The diary texts can also be exported to Microsoft Word in order to analyze them. Conversely, time series data can also be imported into the SNS for analysis and visualization.

At present, the SNS contains the following operations for time series analysis:

- *Dynamic complexity.* Dynamic complexity is composed of a fluctuation and a distribution value (see Appendix). Complexity is calculated in a moving window of freely selectable width and displayed as variation in time for each item or factor of a questionnaire. To determine significance, a 95% or 99% confidence interval that refers to the distribution of prior complexity values can be used to define the significance threshold of the current dynamic complexity value (see Figure 11; for the algorithm, see Schiepek & Strunk, 2010).
- *Complexity resonance diagrams.* When transforming the complexity values into a rainbow color scale and plotting the complexity values, now corresponding to colors, you can choose to scale the color diagram to the actual maximum value (see Figure 17) or any value of your choice (see Figure 18). These diagrams are called complexity resonance diagrams (CRDs) because they show in which items and factors changes in complexity emerge simultaneously (e.g., during critical instabilities). In addition to the direct digitalization of complexity values in color, CRDs are also available with three different significance levels (significance is determined within the respective time series – auto-calibration), where the significant complexity values are marked in light grey, medium grey, and black.

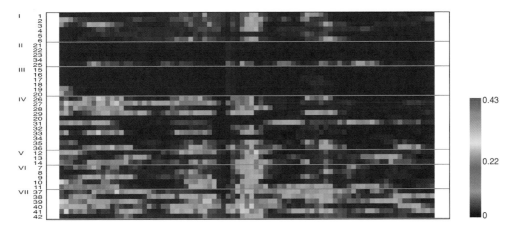

Figure 17

Complexity resonance diagram of Ms. B's course of therapy (see the case study in Chapter 7). Each row represents one TPQ item, grouped by the seven factors described in Haken und Schiepek (2010, pp. 363ff.). The dynamic complexity values here are color-coded, ranging from 0.00 (dark blue) to the maximum value (.43 in this case, dark red). Within most factors we see a vertical structure of increased complexity. The two vertical structures in the middle correspond to the critical instabilities described in the case study (Chapter 7). Deviating from this pattern are the complexity values of the factors II ("climate and atmosphere at the clinic") and III ("relationship quality/openness/trust in the therapist") that are continuously low (dark blue), which indicates a constantly good therapeutic relationship and a feeling of safety on the ward (also with regard to fellow patients).

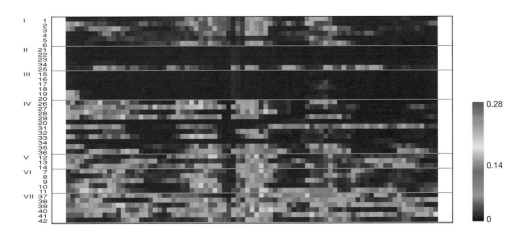

Figure 18

Complexity resonance diagram of Ms. B's course of therapy. The dynamic complexity values are color-coded, ranging from 0.00 (dark blue) to an arbitrary value of .28 (dark red). Values greater than .28 are also coded in dark red. In this calibration, the contrasts between high and low complexities are easier to detect visually.

- *Permutation entropy.* With this method, the probability of sequence patterns of consecutive values (sequence- and word-length, respectively, can be freely selected) of a time series section is calculated using Shannon information. The size relations of consecutive values are ranked at the ordinal level (algorithm in Bandt & Pompe, 2002; Schiepek & Strunk, 2010). Just like dynamic complexity, permutation entropy is displayed over time.
- *Recurrence plots.* This method identifies recurrent patterns of time series in a time × time diagram (Eckmann, Oliffson Kamphorst, & Ruelle, 1987; Orsucci et al., 2006; Webber & Zbilut, 1994). Time series are embedded in a phase-space with time-delay coordinates, with color-coded Euclidean distances between the vector values (distance matrix). Alternatively, the distances can be binary coded according to a selected threshold (recurrence plots; see Figure 19). Different patterns and their transients (periods of critical instability) become apparent. Recurrence plots and CRDs show frequently complementary patterns: periods without recurrent dynamics (out-of-attractor dynamics) correspond to periods of critical instabilities, and hence, increased dynamic complexity.
- *Syncronization patterns.* The absolute (sign-independent) values of inter-item correlations of a questionnaire are averaged within a moving window and presented as average correlation strength over time. This is a measure of coherence of the dynamics. The changes in inter-item correlations are presented in a triangular correlation matrix with color-coded strength of the correlations (from –1 [dark red] over 0 [white] to +1 [dark green]). The correlation matrices can be calculated with a freely selectable time window. A marker can be dragged along the time points to display the change in synchronization patterns over time and up to four matrices can be displayed simultaneously (see Figure 25).

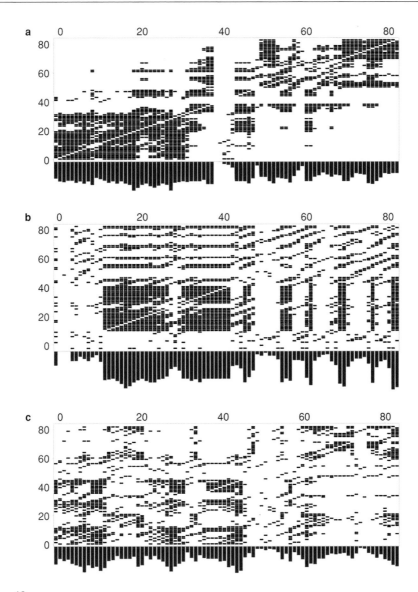

Figure 19

Recurrence plots of a patient's time series data (Ms. B., see Chapter 7). (a) Item 25 of the TPQ: "In contact with my fellow patients, I feel tense" (see time series in Figure 21), (b) Item 31 of the TPQ: "joy" (see Figure 21), (c) factor I of the TPQ: "therapeutic progress/confidence/self-efficacy." Each item/factor was embedded into a three-dimensional phase space with delay 1 (x – 1, x – 2, x – 3). Radius: 23 (Item 25), 25 (Item 31), 29 (factor I). We see critical instability (transients with little recurrence, i.e., very few dots) with a change in dynamical pattern following the instability. The data relate to the case study in Chapter 7; see also Figures 17, 18, 23, and 24).

Chapter 7

Case Study

The following inpatient case study illustrates essential elements of SPM and change monitoring.

7.1 Problems and Resources

The patient, Ms. B., who is approximately 30 years old, is wearing a sporty outfit and has short hair. At first glance, it is impossible to tell that, for many years, she has experienced recurring depressive episodes. On admission, she reports constant ruminations, a significant lack of motivation, existential anxiety about the future, extreme inner restlessness, a lack of feeling and emotional numbness, as well as depersonalization and derealization episodes. At the start of her therapy, she suffers considerably from the fact that she has no real feelings and from "indescribable" sadness.

Ms. B. has been married for seven years and has a daughter of preschool age. She reports no significant problems with her child, but chronic tension in her marriage. She does a great deal for her husband; overindulges him, supports him in his hobbies, drives him to places, and, in general, attempts to fulfill his every wish. Consequently, she never has any time for herself, and she has to put herself last on a continual basis. She reports that she has been used to this pattern from childhood. Also, in order to receive the least bit of attention from her strict and demanding father, she has always striven to function optimally, employing strong self-discipline at home, at school, and in her sports career. In this way, she developed an extreme capacity for suffering that allowed her to succeed in her goals. She represented "successful suffering," as she herself expressed it (for example, in endurance sports), and she also learned to derive advantage from undesirable activities. She excelled in developing these survival strategies, but her vitality and lust for life were left behind. Furthermore, her social contacts served only a functional significance to generate performance. She felt permanently under pressure and developed a feeling of helplessness and fear of loss: if she didn't function perfectly, she would risk losing every single emotional attachment she had to her parents. Because of this, she was never able to develop a stable sense of self-esteem.

She only has very few concrete memories of her childhood, but she remembers that, already as a child, she often felt so sad that she wanted to "jump out of the window." She lived a lot in daydreams and her own fantasy world and, even today, retreating into the world of novels was and is very important to her. However, as well as these stress factors in her life, she is also able to name some resources and competencies during the resources interview. She claims she is a good listener and that it is easy for her to pay attention to both rational and social circumstances. She also mentions patience as one of her strengths and, in particular, that she is a good mother. However, regarding her role as mother, she also strongly

MY PERSONAL RESOURCES												
RESOURCE	0	1	2	3	4	5	6	7	8	9	10	R
Being a good listener					S		P				G	10
Attentiveness						S			P		G	10
Lust for life	S	P									G	10
Patience						S			P		G	10
Capacity for suffering				G							S, P	0
Travelling		S				P					G	8
Self-esteem	S								P		G	10
Sociability			S						P		G	9
Being a good mom						S					P, G	10
Intuition	S		P								G	10

Figure 20
The resources described by Ms. B. during the resources interview, displayed in the style of the resources interview form.

doubts whether she is optimally in tune with her child, considering her emotional numbness and sadness, as well as her current stay in the psychotherapy clinic (this explains why, at this point, she only awards herself a 5 – on a scale of 0 to 10 – for the trait "being a good mom" in the resources interview). Intuition and lust for life are just as important to her as other resources, but, so far, these could only be developed at a low level: Here, her potential (P) is very small. For years, her self-esteem has been lying considerably below the potential (though at least such a potential exists, which seems miraculous considering the description of her childhood). This is also true for her social skills and her desire to be in company. Her potential and actual capacity for suffering lie at the top of the scale, but her goal is to drastically reduce this resource, which used to be helpful and central to her biography but is also central to her current problem system (see Figure 26). Figure 20 shows her resources profile as established in a resources interview.

As her therapy goals, Ms. B. names improving her self-esteem, increasing her self-confidence, re-connecting with her inner liveliness and under-developed intuition (in contrast to her inner numbness), improving her ability to tolerate conflict, and improving contact with her own feelings (again, in general, as well as being able to assess them). An important current topic is her relationship to her husband, which is dominated by regularly occurring strong conflicts. Despite her efforts to do everything for him, she still feels under-valued, un-acknowledged and, furthermore, controlled. Mr. B. does not seem to understand her condition, but Ms. B. does describe her husband as a very reliable father. Ms. B describes their daughter as lively, happy, and generally unproblematic. Her siblings and mother support her, even though she sometimes feels that the contact is strained.

The Resources Interview

At the beginning, the interviewer explains to the client what the term "resource" means. Examples are used to show that it can be very diverse; for example, personal competencies and skills, significant others, social relationships, material resources, ideas, visions, memories, spirituality and religion, and so on.

Then the client's current challenges and goals in life are assessed, and the role the resources should play in reaching those goals and mastering the challenges.

The next step is for the client to identify her/his resources and to provide one or two examples of each. The aim is to induce a cognitive-emotional resources state or a resources- and solution-trance. In many cases, providing a detailed description of the exemplary sceneries triggers associations with further resources. The client is encouraged to identify and describe further resources; in most cases, even with very depressed people, 10 to 20 resources can be named and experienced in narratives.

The client notes the resources on an empty form and, after this, rates them on a scale of 0 to 10 according to four aspects: current state (S), potential (maximum occurrence so far or latent, but not used disposability) (P), goal (where should the resource lie after a certain time, e.g., at the end of therapy) (G), and relevance. It is worth noting that the goal (G) for future occurrence of a resource can be lower than the current state (S), when a resource occurrence should be limited or reduced (often while at the same time boosting other resources). A detailed description of the procedure can be found in Schiepek and Cremers (2003), as well as the convergent and divergent validity of the interview assessed using different clinical measures.

7.2   Therapy Progress With Order Transition

Ms. B. is very quick to embrace the therapy concept, which comprises individual and group therapy sessions. The therapy options offered – music therapy, art therapy, Nordic walking, Chi Gong, and psychodrama – interest her and do not overburden her emotionally. In the clinic, she feels secure, safe, and well supported (Figure 21, Item 21). Working with her therapists, especially her main therapist, is a success from the beginning (Figure 21, Item 15). For her, the generic principle 1 (stability and experience of safety) is realized from the outset.

The experience of first therapy successes supports her feeling that she is in the right hands and receiving sensible therapy offers (generic principle 3), which makes her want to engage in them (generic principle 4). Although Ms. B. was suffering from considerable emotional numbness and a feeling of emptiness at the outset, music therapy and body therapy soon helped her to perceive feelings and her own body. This furthered her interest in and curiosity about the therapy topics (Figure 21, Item 11). A noteworthy quality of feeling characterizes her experiences, particularly during the first two weeks: It is not only her sadness that re-occurs at a high level (Figure 21, Item 26), but also her feelings of anger and rage (Item 27). During her first week in the clinic, she notes in her SNS diary: (1) "Today the first individual music therapy session. I liked it a lot, because I felt a lot of aggression and rage within me today" (the times of the diary entries are marked with numbers in Figure 22). When looking at her entries together with the therapist, she realizes that, contrary to her self-image of emotional numbness, she can indeed feel emotions. It

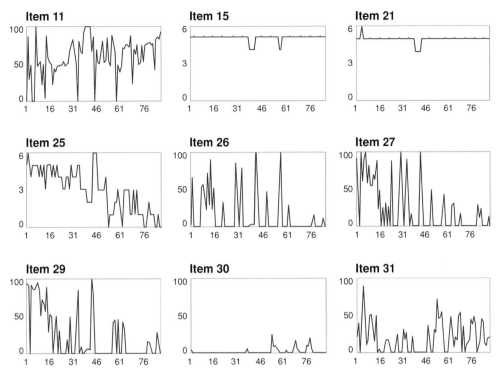

Figure 21
The dynamics of some of Ms. B.'s TPQ items: "Extent of my interest in therapy topics and content" (Item 11), "I experience the work with the therapist as helpful" (Item 15), "In the clinic, I feel safe and supported" (Item 21), "In contact with my fellow patients, I feel tense today" (Item 25), "Grief" (Item 26), "anger/rage" (Item 27), "anxiety" (Item 29), "self-esteem" (Item 30), "joy" (Item 31).

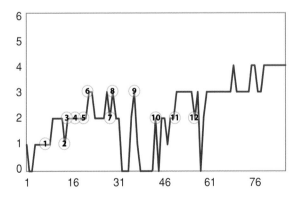

Figure 22
The development of Item 1 ("I can increasingly solve my problems on my own"). Almost every day, Ms. B. made diary entries following her item ratings of the TPQ. Marked are the times of the entries which are cited and consecutively numbered in the text.

is not only negative emotions (e.g., anxiety, Item 29) that she can feel; she is also able to experience happiness and joy (Item 31). Her self-esteem (Item 30) is still virtually nonexistent, and it takes well into the second half of the therapy and some critical developments until this changes a little for the better.

After two weeks, Ms. B. is increasingly able to voice her inner uneasiness, the adverse effect of her emotional numbness, her self-doubts, and also the strain she feels due to the whole situation: (2) "Today was very difficult for me. I felt extremely uneasy. I can't really assess my situation, which limits me even more. My self-doubts were overly high today and because of that also my inner listlessness. I finally want to live again and feel myself with all my senses, so that my self-esteem is in balance with myself again, so that I can better judge what is good for me and what is not." The next day, during dance and movement therapy, an inner shell seemed to break open: (3) "Was at dance and movement today and that was very interesting. For the first time I felt a smile and, afterwards, I had water in my eyes. I have not experienced anything like that in a very long time and it made me happy." However, during the following few days, it is again her distress regarding her emotional numbness that plays a primary role. (4) "I am at a loss about my missing feelings, that is really stressful to me. […] It's really hard for me to run around without any feelings all day." Such differences in the daily assessments can be interpreted as the beginnings of a critical instability (generic principle 5).

Narratives of the individual therapy sessions are characterized by more emotional content from this point on until the end of therapy. In this case, as in many others, the narratives first change in the SNS diaries – indicated by the described emotional qualities, the choice of words or the topics and content – and only afterwards in the direct communication of the therapy conversation in individual or group therapy sessions. Thus, the diaries – given that the client consents to the therapist reading them – can be used sensitively to expose the client to new contents, as well as to emotions and topics that are currently un-lived, schismatic, not (yet) perceptible, or not (yet) communicable. Unlike interpretations or hypotheses of the therapist, these are not the therapist's impressions, but rather texts written by the client herself.

The more she is able to experience her emotions, the more intensely Ms. B. perceives her relationship problems, and she soon expresses the desire for a couples session, which is scheduled promptly. The topic is how her depression affects her relationship and family. Mr. B. is motivated and Ms. B. agrees that the counseling session was a good start. In the following individual sessions, Ms. B. reflects more on her own contributions to the relationship problems and, in the context of the marriage conflicts, she starts to perceive herself better. For the first time, she can draw connections between the slights and degradations she has suffered in the past and her current experiences. Ms. B. is very motivated to learn how to better recognize and perceive her own patterns; see Items 1 (Figure 22), 6 (Figure 23), and 11 (Figure 21), as well as factors V and VI (Figure 24).

Instead of emotional numbness, she now writes about emotional chaos: (5) "Had a bad headache again today, hands shaking very much and inner uneasiness, so that the very slightest bodily motion made me gasp for air. During the day, I am very tired and, in the evening, I have trouble falling asleep. I'm very much missing my drive lately and I am tired of my emotional chaos."

In week four of the therapy, Ms. B. expresses the strong feelings she had when saying goodbye to her daughter after a weekend spent at home with her family: (6) "At home at night after having put K. to bed, K. kept crying because she didn't want me to leave, wanted me to stay with her and that broke my heart."

To develop an understanding for her "no-being-able-to-feel-herself," Ms. B. searches for childhood memories and the feelings hidden within these. Ms. B. uses and thereby improves her ability to mentalize. She describes tellingly: (7) "Today was an interesting day.

There were several times when I tried to feel myself, but I couldn't feel anything. Started a new book today and [...] I kept trying to look into myself and to perceive emotions in certain situations, but it does not work. I wanted to reflect on my childhood and see how I perceived the whole situation, but I do not even feel it in my body and, if I feel anything at all, it is all the pain that is inside me. I wish to feel alive again, that I become self-confident and self-assured as a woman." She values the SNS work, the mentalization processes during the daily completion of the TPQ, and reflecting on her emotional development, particularly when comparing her emotional changes illustrated by the graphs of the items and the specific experiences during that day.

After approximately five weeks of therapy, the process reaches a point of critical instability. Ms. B. is personally criticized by another patient (see the local maximum in Item 25 [Figure 21]), and, as well as this, she argues with her husband. The argument centered on Ms. B.'s self-denying services (e.g., playing the "taxi driver" until late at night). It was during a party with acquaintances that the conflict with her husband broke out. Until then, she had (for the first time) felt relatively stable, and was at home for the weekend. However, her husband decided to continue socializing with his friends at another venue and no longer looked after her. To her surprise, Ms. B's friends and acquaintances at the party did not enquire about her time at the therapy clinic. She felt degraded, unappreciated, ignored and she experienced shame, embarrassment, hate, rage, and anger. Her diary entry reads as follows: (8) "I was very emotional today and could not calm down." Weeks of improvements are followed by a crisis that lasts almost two weeks, during which Ms. B. feels very low at times, e.g., (9): "Today was a very bad day for me. I cried all day and felt as if something inside me was dying, was drowsy and my legs were shaking." Retrospectively, she claims to have felt *real sadness*. The day after this entry (Entry 9), during her individual therapy session, Ms. B. describes the relevant feelings, emotions, thoughts, bodily reactions, and behavior patterns in a very differentiated and self-reflected manner (10): "Today I was under a lot of pressure and shying away from conflict all day. Whenever I realized I had to adopt a position towards something, I stopped breathing and my heart started racing. I was afraid of criticism and, looking back, I can see that I got all worked up about it without any obvious reason and I took a very long time until I calmed down! I should work up the courage more often to ask once again when something is not clear in my mind and not to always refer everything to myself. That is a tough one for me lately."

This phase of critical instability in the therapy process manifests itself in almost all items (see Figures 21 and 22). Figure 23 shows that she perceives this therapy phase as unsuccessful regarding reaching her therapy goals, her discomfort increases (after a short phase with considerably reduced discomfort) and she feels helpless in confronting her problems. Figure 24 shows the subscales of the TPQ over time. It is not only dynamic complexity that increases during this phase; the Depression-Anxiety-Stress Scale (Lovibond & Lovibond, 1995) that is completed weekly also shows increased values (Figure 16). However, this therapy crisis does not afflict the therapeutic relationship in any major way or the perceived support in the clinic (see Items 21 and 15 in Figure 21). This means that, on this occasion, we are dealing with an example of *destabilization in the context of stability*.

The phase of critical instability marks an order transition to a changed cognition-emotion-behavior pattern. After a short time (just under two weeks), Ms. B. was able to overcome the crisis, mainly through her own efforts. For the first time, she clearly experiences positive feelings. She is able to enjoy a day at the lake together with her daughter "to the full"; that is, predominantly without feelings of guilt. Furthermore, she experiences

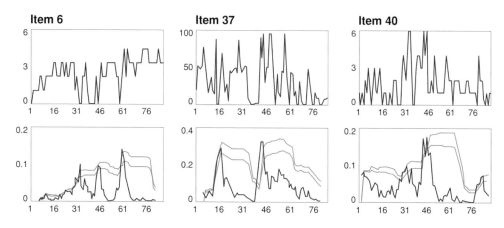

Figure 23

Top row: Evolution of Item 6 ("With reference to my personal goals I perceived myself as successful [=6]/unsuccessful [=0] today"), Item 37 (level of "problem intensity"), and Item 40 ("Today I felt helpless in the face of my problems"). Bottom row: The dynamic complexity values of these items (calculated over a moving window of 7 data points [=days]). The two additional curves (light blue) represent a 95% and 99% confidence interval based on 21 data points.

an afternoon spent together with her daughter, whom she collected from kindergarten, as "happy." In therapy, she deals intensively with her behavior and emotional feelings; the therapeutic work acquires a new quality and intensity. Contacts with her fellow patients are now much more relaxed (Figure 21, Item 25). It is also worth mentioning that Ms. and Mr. B. decide to start couples counseling.

The critical instability of this order transition can be seen in the development of the dynamic complexity (Figures 23 and 24) and across all items in the synoptic illustration in the complexity-resonance diagram (Figure 17 and 18). The dynamic complexity process of each item (calculated in a moving window of 7 days) is here translated into a color scale and built up line by line. The fact that the therapeutic relationship remains generally stable over time is depicted in the blue (= low) complexity values of the items that indicate the same. Figure 19 shows the order transition in the recurrence plots of the items "tension towards fellow patients," "happiness," and "therapeutic progress" (factor I). When looking at the intercorrelation of all items in a moving window containing seven measurement points, we see an increased synchronization between the items of the TPQ; that is, between the experiences of the client that are determined by the survey (Figure 25). This phenomenon – that synchronization increases and thus only one (or very few) order parameter becomes dominant in the whole cognitive-emotional dynamic of the intrapsychic therapy system during periods of critical instability – has been observed in many therapies (Haken & Schiepek, 2010, p. 407 ff.).

After at approximately eight weeks, Ms. B. begins to experience strong headaches, which lead to another setback: (11) "Worked on myself today, but unfortunately, the headache was stronger than me." In Figure 24, for instance, this crisis is represented by the last distinct spike of the factor dynamics I, V, and VI (down) and VII (up).

Despite this short setback, Ms. B. is highly motivated to use the remaining time in the clinic to continuously work on herself: (11) "I am intent on using the last weeks to do this. I want to finally get to know myself well and be fully alive. I hope to find myself during my

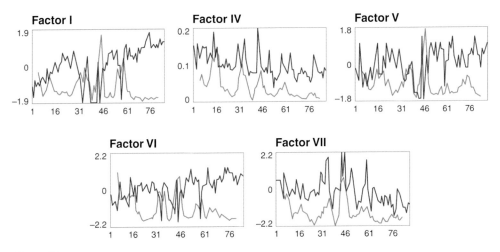

Figure 24
Evolution of the subscales "therapeutic progress/confidence/self-efficacy" (factor I), "dysphoric affectivity/self-relatedness" (factor IV), "broadening in perspective and innovation" (factor V), "intensity of working on problems" (factor VI), and "discomfort and pressure" (factor VII) (blue). These factors are based on an older factor analysis of the TPQ (see Haken & Schiepek, 2010, p. 363ff.). The dynamic complexity values are also plotted (red; calculated over a moving window of 7 data points [=days]).

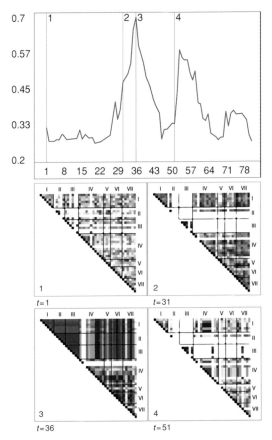

Figure 25
Time series of the inter-correlations of all TPQ items, grouped by the 7 factors described in Haken and Schiepek (2010). The correlations (n = 42 items, equaling n(n − 1)/2 = 861 correlations) are calculated over a moving window of 7 data points. Only the absolute values of the correlations are included in the average calculations. The curve is an indicator for the synchronization of the whole system (in this case: all items). As also demonstrated by other sets of data, synchronization increases in temporal proximity to instabilities. Shown are the inter-correlation matrixes at four points in time during therapy. The matrices display both the values and the directions of the correlations in color (intensity of green: positive correlation; intensity of red: negative correlation, white: null-correlation or calculation not possible because of zero variance). At the beginning, inter-correlations are low and there is little structure. In time, we see more structure (e.g., negative correlations between the items of factor I "therapeutic progress/confidence/self-efficacy" and factor VII "discomfort and pressure"). The white bands of the factors II and III represent the stability of these communal factors (little variance and little correlation with other aspects of the client's experience). With regard to content, this means that the relationship to therapist and fellow patients is hardly affected by the patient's emotional changes (see generic principle 1).

remaining time here in the clinic, to be able to drop all facades." She stabilizes at a higher level in her confidence, success experience regarding her personal goals, and other therapy-relevant aspects (see Figures 21, 22, 23, and 24). Despite, or precisely because of, the high intensity of problem-solving (Figure 24, factor VI) and realization willingness (Figure 24, factor V), this phase is followed once again by phases of self-deprecation and self-hate. She is unhappy with her body and appearance: (12) "I experienced today as very turbulent. [...] I feel like a stranger in my own body, don't feel good. I feel queasy when I see that I do something I don't like again."

Once again, an extensive examination of the self-esteem topic follows. Ms. B. remembers doing lots of sports as a child, having been successful in several disciplines and having won prizes. However, these achievements did not receive recognition from her father, so she was unable to recognize her own successes and use them to develop a more positive self-image. Ms. B., who has always taken care of how she looks, occasionally develops real joy in her attractive appearance. And she feels happy when she receives positive feedback in this regard. In the last three weeks of therapy, we see a definite stabilization. Despite setbacks in mood, which mainly manifest in headaches, on most days, positive feelings affect her experiences. She goes on day trips with her daughter, engages in free-time activities (which she assesses as positive), and can finally enjoy many things again. Ms. B. perceives the day she is discharged from the clinic as very positive, is optimistic, and sees the future as bright. The couples counseling is already planned for the time following her discharge from the clinic.

7.3   System Modeling

Ms. B.'s high motivation and interest in the therapy contents could be used to perform idiographic system modeling in the last third of the therapy. In many therapies, idiographic system models are developed at some point; namely, when a case formulation is generated. In Ms. B.'s case, the phase of intensive examination of herself and her past, during which she was finally able to access her memories and feelings, was the appropriate time to conduct the reconstructive method. Figure 26 shows her personal (idiographic) model.

The starting point and setting for her model was her current life situation. She described her experience and behavior towards her partner. Among other things, she discussed her desire for harmony and her fear of loss (which made her do things she didn't want to do and set up her life in an undesirable way). She had been optimizing her capacity for pain and her skill to succeed in and benefit from undesired activities from her childhood onwards. This is why it was important for her to identify the parallels between this model, which was developed according to her present life situation, and the experiences and survival strategies she remembers from her childhood. She realized several dynamics and process patterns in her problem model and repeatedly produced obstacles on her way to gaining lust for life and higher self-esteem.

Thus, the system model provided starting points for changes, if only because it allowed her to clearly identify her own share in the development. As a result of the compiled relations and the "variableness" – that is, the values of the individual components can change in both directions – system models are ambiguous patterns par excellence: They show how problems develop and stabilize, but they also illustrate that and how it can be the reverse – how synergy effects can be used to come to a solution – and where starting points for changes are.

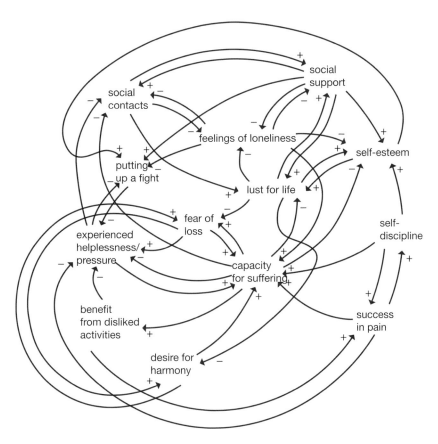

Figure 26
The idiographic system model developed together with Ms. B. This was the basis for the personalized process survey she used after discharge. The variables of the model are rated daily using visual analog scales (see Figure 27).

In this case, the reason for system modeling was, among other things, the development of a personal survey that contains the components of the system model as items and questions, respectively. Within the SNS, the questionnaire editor facilitates a quick implementation of such personalized surveys (in this case using visual analog scales). Ms. B. used the questionnaire during her inpatient stay and also for six weeks afterwards. It allowed her to focus further on the topics that are of importance to her and to document occurring changes. Figure 27 displays the process of the daily assessments of the personal items continued at home.

In both diagrams of the figure, the day of dismissal is marked by a vertical line. We can see a considerable increase in perceived pressure and the feeling of being left alone as well as fear of loss – emotions that are obviously more pronounced at home than in the safe environment of the clinic. The addressed motivators of her capacity for pain (namely, her wish for harmony), her fear of loss, and the feeling of being left alone score very highly in the first three weeks after discharge, with slight decreases following. After approximately three weeks, her self-esteem increases from nonexistent to perceivable. This is marked externally by a visit to the hairdresser and, internally, by feeling her femininity and beginning to like

Idiographic System Modeling

In system modeling, the patient typically begins by describing the problem scenario of the last weeks and months. In order to reach a deeper understanding, the therapist can inquire about specific details and broach the issue of problem-solving and coping strategies, exceptions to the problem, and constructive ways to deal with it. While the patient talks, the therapist takes notes of the aspects, partial processes or terms that can later be used as model components. Afterwards, the client and therapist look through the noted terms, sum them up, or modify their meanings. It is important that they both understand the terms and word choices and that the client approves them as being appropriate. Conceptual components of a system model should be variables, namely, factors that can change over time (e.g., within hours, days, or weeks). Individual people ("John," "Mary") or events are unsuitable. It is possible, on the other hand, to use variables that express the relationship with a person (e.g., the perceived closeness to Mary or the intensity of the conflicts with John) or the perceived intensity of a memory of a certain event. The variables stand for intraindividual or interpersonal aspects of a more complex system, e.g., cognitions, emotions, motives, behavior, and so on. They are named using either psychological or everyday terms. In most cases, psychological variables are "theoretical constructs." The next step is to try and graphically depict the effects of the single components on other components on a flip chart. Arrows are used to show the effects of the components on each other, in the most straightforward cases qualified by a + or a –, with + denoting a positive relation (e.g., "the more she experiences lust for life, the higher the self-esteem" or the other way round: "the less she experiences lust for life, the lower the self-esteem"). – denotes a negative relation (e.g., "the more she is able to see the use of disliked activities, the better she can reduce feelings of helplessness and pressure" or the other way round: "the less she is able to see the use of disliked activities, the more helplessness and pressures she feels;" "low performance induces feelings of guilt" or "high performance reduces feelings of guilt") (see Figure 26).

There are several forms interactions or activation/inhibition loops between variables can take:

- Direct interactions between variables (e.g., "lust for life" and "self-esteem" or "success in pain" and "self-discipline") activating and triggering each other.
- Loops between several components (e.g., "lust for life" could, for instance, by way of a more positive outward appearance, lead to "social support" enabling more "social contacts," which in turn increases "lust for life;" or: "capacity for suffering" reduces "lust for life," which increases "feelings of loneliness;" the more Ms. B. feels lonely, the less she is able to "stand up for herself;" that is, to keep clear of expectations that don't do her any good, which, in turn, increases "pressure" and "perceived helplessness," so that she has to increase her "capacity for suffering" in order to survive; Figure 26).
- Recursion of a variable to itself (autocatalytic effect).

Increased crosslinking of the components makes it possible to see connections that were previously unnoticed or were only considered unilateral cause-and-effect-relations (true to the motto: "x is to blame for y").

herself and her look (especially as she receives positive feedback on and appreciation for her appearance). She now becomes more selective regarding her social contacts: She reduces "bad" contacts and turns towards more supportive and beneficial contacts. She learns accordingly to respect her social needs and "to say no."

Several of the relations worked out in the system model are now confirmed by her daily assessments. More and more, however, it is not only the stabilizing and consolidating in-

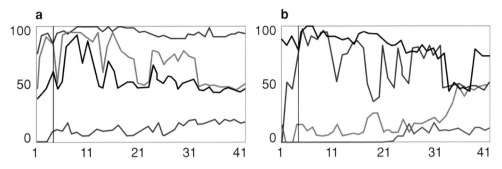

Figure 27
Time series of a subset of items of Ms. B.'s personalized survey. (a) "desire for harmony" (blue), "fear of loss" (red), "perceived pressure and helplessness" (black), "lust for life/joy/spontaneity" (pink); (b) "capacity for suffering" (black), "I feel left alone" (blue), "I can defend myself/I feel strong" (red), Item 10: "self-esteem" (pink). The vertical line marks the date of discharge.

teractions of the model that are active, but also those that gravitate towards change (e.g., being able to defend herself, having more lust for life, less fear of loss, less pressure and helplessness, including the respective relations between these variables). Ms. B. feels liberated by the idea that she is not essentially dependent on her partnership. She intends to look carefully at the developments that take place in couples counseling (due to begin in the immediate future) and to do her part in it, but she is autonomous enough to not have to accept every result. Regarding her autonomy development, it is not only significant that she has now commenced her own activities, but also that she is now slowly releasing herself from feelings of guilt regarding her role as a mother.

In therapeutic follow-up care, the long-term sustainability of therapy effects that usually cannot be taken for granted can be supported by the daily assessment of the learned and acquired strategies, approaches, and solutions. The process pattern made visible by means of the SNS can furthermore be used as the basis for communication in ambulatory therapy sessions, which can be held face-to-face, via phone, email, and Internet.

Chapter 8

The Interconnection of Monitoring and Therapy

The case study presented in Chapter 7 focuses mainly on the client's processes of change and not so much on therapy techniques and therapeutic offers. In the case of Ms. B., a range of therapy techniques were used, which exposed her to a range of stimuli that suited her current development and the acute demands of the process. The generic principles are a permanent help in deciding which therapeutic methods to select. However, the therapeutic approaches offered were not systemic in the common sense of the word. As outlined above (see Section 2.1), techniques per se do not add very much to the therapy success and, consequently, we do not use them to define what systemic therapy consists of in a school-independent integrative conception.

However, an essential part of systemic therapy is to understand any particular case in a way that illuminates the various interdependent components of the system and to monitor the system's dynamics. In addition to systemic case formulation ("clarification perspective" according to Grawe, 1995), this enables us to identify not only starting points for changes and combinations as well as synergies of such input points, but also the dynamics of the events resulting from the interactions between the variables of the system model (or rather the aspects of the psychosocial system represented by them).

8.1 Therapeutic Effects of Feedback Systems

Using the process representation available in the SNS, therapists can recognize patterns that would not be visible to the unaided eye or to one's intuition; for instance, critical instabilities, changes in synchronization patterns or dynamic order transitions. These are patterns and pattern changes that feature no (or much weaker) experiential "qualia" than, for example, the emotional expression of another person or other direct communication signals.

We are specialized in the perception and interpretation of emotional expression, intentions, or needs of the person we are interacting with in the here and now per the mirror neuron system or theory of mind functions of our brain (Rizzolatti & Craighero, 2004), but we are not specialized in the perception of the dynamic attributes of complex systems, especially if they unfold over a long period of time. As previously mentioned, a study by Lambert et al. (2005) showed that therapists were unable to recognize emerging setbacks, even in regular contact with their clients. However, a simple monitoring system, which measured the symptom strain and functional impairment of the clients relatively loosely (that is, during each of the therapy sessions), was able to do precisely that. Specific instructions for the therapists (so-called "clinical support tool") then avoided dropouts and setbacks.

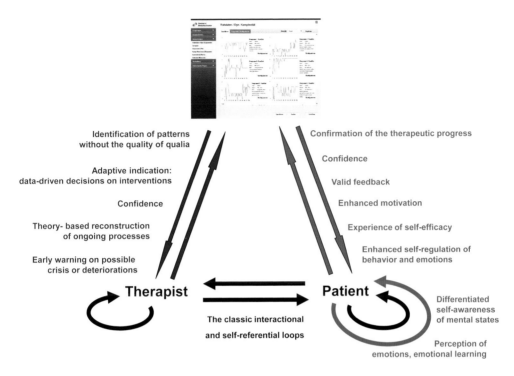

Figure 28
Potential beneficial therapy effects of the SNS for therapists and clients.

The SNS can be used to reach databased, adaptive indication decisions that help manage the therapy process. The SNS feedback gives the therapist certainty (which he or she can in turn pass on to the client) and a theoretical foundation for the procedure. Figure 28 shows the potential effects of the SNS on therapists and clients.

The feedback reassures the client about the chosen path, provides him/her with certainty, and confirms their emotions and experiences as valid – an experience that is not at all self-evident in many clients with early attachment and social resonance impairments. Motivation and commitment to their personal development process can increase as well as the experience of self-efficacy, which is meditated by the immediate visibility of the effects of their own action on their experience. Self-regulation learning processes (Kanfer, Reinecker, & Schmelzer, 2006) are facilitated by timely feedback.

Daily self-assessment supports mentalization processes, because it asks for a differentiated self-perception and perception of others (especially of their emotions). It is particularly important for clients with lasting strong emotions (e.g., grief, anger), with experienced emotional emptiness, or with impaired emotional regulation to differentiate daily between different emotions and to reflect on related cognitions or situative triggers. This is a learning process in the perception of emotions, mentalization capacity, attentiveness, and meta-cognitive competency. Clients describe their daily work with the SNS as a small personal therapy session, quality time, a calming ritual, or a "secularized evening prayer." For many, it is a meaningful time of contemplation and reflection on the day; anything but the boring completion of a survey form, especially when a personalized questionnaire is used. Furthermore, regarding the immune activation and emotional effects of expressive writing (e.g., diaries; Pennebaker & Chung, 2007), we can assume that the SNS has not only diagnostic uses, but also therapeutic effects. It is possible that these occur as a result of the mechanisms mentioned previously, but also by focusing continuously (e.g., daily) on the change process, by boosting feedback-mediated motivation, and by strengthening the therapeutic relationship. Although counter-intuitive at first glance, our experience thus far shows that the use of the SNS brings about a more intense, as opposed to a less intense, therapeutic relationship. Among other things, this is the result of communicating interest in the client's development process in the triangular situation displayed in Figure 15 (client, therapist, screen).

These therapeutic functions should be investigated intensively in the near future, as well as the strengths and therapeutic mechanisms of monitoring and feedback. There is evidence for the therapeutic effect of feedback and monitoring systems that are used considerably less often (that is, per therapy session) than laid out in SPM. Lambert (2010) identifies that improvements by using feedback systems are expected in all clients – not only when setbacks or dropouts are emerging – and that this doesn't involve prolonging the therapy. In a study by Miller, Duncan, Brown, Sorrell, & Chalk (2006), the percentage of improvement was at 34% before a feedback system was implemented and 47% thereafter; the percentage of setbacks was reduced from 19% to 8%. A comparison of a group receiving "treatment as usual" with a group receiving "feedback-assisted psychotherapy" revealed effect sizes (Cohen's d) of .54 (Study 1) and .49 (Study 2) in support of feedback-assisted therapy (Reese, Norsworthy, & Rowlands, 2009).

Sparks and Duncan (2010) also emphasize the relevance of feedback and monitoring systems in couples counseling and family therapy. A comparison study with couples randomly assigned to a feedback or nonfeedback condition yielded an effect size of .50 (Anker, Duncan, & Sparks, 2009). Clients in the "treatment as usual" group were categorized as "responder" in 42% of cases (percentage of both partners being "responder" was 23%) and, in the feedback group, this occurred in 65% of cases (percentage of both partners being "responder" was 51%). In the feedback condition, four times as many couples reached a "nondistressed" stress level. These effects were still in place at the 6-month follow-up; in the feedback condition, only half as many couples split up compared to the "treatment as usual" condition. An interesting observation is that, in this study, feedback particularly supported therapists whose clients would have shown only small- or medium-sized effects during regular procedures (without feedback). These therapists could obtain much better results when using feedback.

The SNS has also been adopted in couples counseling, and a specific couples counseling questionnaire has been developed on the basis of the TPQ (Fornaro, 2009; Ulrich, 2011). A research project carried out at the Ludwig Maximilians University, Munich, Germany identified interesting synchronization processes between the two partners, for example, simultaneous or slightly delayed changes in dynamical patterns in the recurrence plots. A specific method of process measurement of interpersonal relationships (*relationship pattern analysis/interaction matrice*) is still waiting to be used in clinical practice. This method is based on a mutual assessment of the people involved in the social process, and the items can be generated, defined, and adapted as required. On a Likert scale, the participants rate how pronounced their initiative (sending) was on a certain dimension (e.g., support, stress, flow of information) towards the other person in a reference period; and, similarly, they rate how pronounced they perceived the action of the other person towards themselves on the same dimension (receiving). This results in a color-coded matrix that displays the difference between self-perceived and externally perceived communication (Figure 10). Such ratings can be done repeatedly during the process of interest and the resulting matrixes can be presented in chronological order like a movie. This method can be applied in couples counseling, family therapy, group therapy, team and organizational development, or in business and simulation games.

Without wishing to over-interpret the results presented in this section, we can claim that they indicate that feedback systems have not only diagnostic uses but also therapeutic effects. Sparks and Duncan (2010) claim that such therapeutic effects seem to be independent of the used outcome- and process-measuring instruments. Furthermore, they claim that feedback methods are "generic in nature and not tied to a single therapy modality" (p. 376) and that "feedback improves outcome regardless of the model practiced: the feedback process does not dictate what technique is used but rather is a vehicle to modify any delivered treatment for client benefit" (p. 377). Sparks and Duncan (2010) emphasize that feedback supports therapeutic factors, such as those described in Chapter 2, that it increases interactions between those factors, and that feedback itself can become a central component in the therapeutic system. This component plays a major role in the school-independent, integrative systemic model of psychotherapy (feedback-driven dynamic systems approach).

8.2 SNS-Based Therapy Sessions

According to our experience, frequency and especially quality of feedback conversations and SNS-based therapy interviews are a fundamental precondition for "compliance" (the motivation and commitment to use the SNS) and "self-relatedness" (being willing to engage in self-reflection and the personal development process when working with the SNS). Feedback and therapeutic intervention are here inseparably compounded, and we therefore now often use the term *SNS-based therapy session*. Such SNS-based therapy conversations (see Figure 15) and their supervision should form a substantial part of psychotherapy training from this moment onwards. The starting point is to explain the items/questions of the TPQ at the beginning of therapy or to develop a personalized questionnaire based on the resources interview, idiographic system modeling, and therapy goals. Subsequent conversations always refer back to this, especially when new topics and goals surface during the process. The box below contains practical questions and notes that can be used to conduct SNS-based therapy sessions.

Conducting SNS-Based Therapy Sessions

Already on admission – but certainly after the therapeutic contract and goals are clarified or the case formulation is completed, respectively – the therapist and client can decide together on the items and variables of the TPQ that are most relevant and best represent the client's particular problems or goals (using the configuration function in the SNS). The therapist can consistently refer to these during therapy sessions. To initiate the conversation, the therapist can ask what items have been of particular importance to the client recently.

Questions should be asked openly, so that the client is able to have his/her say at length, and the therapist should refrain from interrupting (except for justifiable exceptions). In preparation for the session, the therapist can print the time series and mark prominent changes in the plots, and, at a later point, she/he can ask the client how she/he interprets the dynamic patterns.

General questions
- How does the client evaluate progress?
- How are symptoms and stress with the problem developing?
- Are symptoms and stress with the problem related to the progress made? (To this, the therapist can, for instance, overlap the time series of the respective items on the monitor.)
- How is therapy motivation?
- What resources did the client activate?
- How does the client see the therapeutic relationship and working alliance?
- How does the client evaluate their relationship with fellow clients (in inpatient or day treatment settings)?
- What conflicts manifest in negative evaluations of these relationships? Are these known transference patterns?

Potential new topics
- Which items represent essential topics, conflicts, and therapy goals of the client?
- Do the time series or diary entries indicate essential topics or problems that were thus far not broached (conflicts, avoidance patterns)?
- How are negative or positive emotions evaluated (e.g., are emotions like anger, rage, or shame assessed as nonexistent permanently or for a longer period of time?)
- How is self-esteem developing?
- Can item progression indicate a new diagnosis (e.g., strong and highly frequent fluctuations in emotions could indicate borderline disorder, or relationship conflicts could indicate attachment problems or traumata)?

Problem solving
The graphs and diary entries can be used to answer the following:
- What are the exceptions to the problem?
- How could the client make changes, solutions, and positive experiences possible?
- What did he or she do in order to achieve this?
- What did others do in order to achieve the improvement?
- Which problem patterns have emerged?
- What resources were used?
- Integrate the information in the functional behavior analysis (internal and external triggers), if one has been done.
- Which dynamics/fluctuations go along with which experiences (e.g., weekdays vs. weekend, good vs. bad days, etc.)?

Many of the interviewing techniques common in solution-focused therapy (de Shazer, 1985; Miller et al., 1996; Walter & Peller, 1992) or hypno-systemic therapy (Schmidt, 2005) can be transferred easily to SNS-based therapy conversations.

Compliments
- What positive feedback can the therapist give the client? What can be reinforced? What kind of praise and positive feedback can the client accept?

Warning signs
- Does the client have enough therapy motivation?
- How does the client rate the item: "A different therapeutical approach would be more suitable for me"?
- No improvements: How to interpret that?
- Is therapy motivation evaluated in a negative way?

- Do we see critical instability coexisting with a low sense of security, little interest in or high fear of therapy topics and contents? (see the traffic light function of the SNS, Figure 12).

Next steps
- What are the next meaningful steps? What does the client propose? What can the client do to accomplish these steps?
- What exercises or experiments come to mind?

Emotions
- What emotions were experienced? Can emotions be differenciated and described?
- How were emotions activated (external causes, internal evaluations, appraisals)?
- In which contexts do the emotions occur?
- Which coping and control strategies could be used?
- How much of a certain emotion (rage, grief, self-esteem) does the client allow him-/ herself?

Instability
- Which items/factors and thereby experiences are affected by destabilizations (see the complexity resonance diagrams in Figures 17 and 18)?
- What kind of instability is it? Constructive instability immediately before new steps or developments? Or do negative affects predominate? What ambivalences accompany it?
- What needs to be prevented? Is a setback to be suspected? Which recurring or negative experiences could be made?
- What chances are there?
- What kind of support or special measures would be helpful?

Synchronization patterns
- Which items are particularly strongly synchronized (positively or negatively)?
- Is, for instance, the symptom course coupled to therapeutic progress/reaching of goals (negatively correlated) or independent?
- Is the evaluation of the therapeutic relationship (positively/negatively) synchronized with symptom course or progress or motivation/process involvement or is it independent of it?

8.3 Reactive Measures

The interlacing of diagnostics and process measurement on the one hand and therapy on the other is a methodological challenge that should not be underestimated. Classically, this is called the *problem of reactive measures*: The measurement itself changes the system's behavior and the subject measured, respectively. There seems to be no escape from this problem, since all currently existing ambulatory assessment and quality management methods rely on the client's self-assessment. Data from the protagonist's perspective are essential, even if evaluations by a third party (e.g., therapist or family members) are collected or physiological measures are taken. Taking the measurement and thereby initiating self-reflection changes the process. However, this is not only true for real-time monitoring measures, but for all data collection processes that call for a conscious involvement of the proband (e.g., questionnaires, tests, interviews, physiological measures, observations) – that is, practially all methods that require *informed consent*. This is not a specific difficulty in ambulatory assessment or therapeutical feedbacks, but of the psychological method in general. Psychology is not about test probands without consciousness, but about reflective, active, and (more or less) cooperative subjects. This continues to be a relevant concern for the philosophy of science and psychological methodology (particulary in this context).

Even more stringent is the problem associated with repeated self-evaluations in psychotherapy, since both valid data *and* reflection- and therapy-supporting effects are expected. This could be interpreted as a contradiction. However, ultimately, it is no more than simply adding a further recurrence loop to a process that is already heavily recurrence-intensive. At this point, it is not possible to make a final assessment on whether the effects of this recurrence loop stay constant or – since, among other things, this is about learning processes (see Figure 28) – are changing themselves and are thus nonstationary and nonergodic. While feedback systems have a welcome therapeutic effect, which – as outlined in this chapter – is not to be underestimated, the generated process data are nevertheless informative, indicative for nonstationary dynamics, and possible to validate using external data (third party reports, clinical impressions) as well as mixed comparisons between different process surveys and data sources.

Process feedback can be seen as having an *amplifying effect* on the dynamics that ordinarily take place. Feedback (linearly or nonlinearly) displays small-detailed processes on a larger scale and thereby catalyzes change processes that might have taken place regardless (*autocatalytic effect*). In the future, we would like to see methodological discourses on this topic as well as more research on the therapeutical effects of feedback systems.

Chapter 9

Conceptual Developments

9.1 Dynamic Pattern Recognition and Process Regulation as Components of Therapeutic Practice

Process monitoring holds a key function in organizing psychotherapy processes (see Figure 29). Classical components of psychotherapy – be it according to a systemic or any other concept – are providing the correct setting, clarifying wishes and therapy goals, undertaking diagnostics and anamnesis (depending on the approach with more or less emphasis on this point), and – this goes without saying – carrying out interventions. To explicitly measure therapy outcome and to document therapy quality using appropriate instruments is still not a given in ambulatory practice. Neither can it be taken for granted, but of importance to be assessed according to need, is the linking-up and coordination of the client's networks (whether from professional or personal contexts, e.g., family members) and other helper systems or facilities that may be required to provide effective follow-up care. In Figure 29, organization and monitoring of follow-up care is presented as part of a meaningful therapeutic approach, especially in inpatient care and day-treatment centers.

Process monitoring, which is performed in order to recognize patterns, is awarded an essential role in this therapeutic approach. By measuring process patterns, information for case formulations can be attained that by far exceed static diagnostic procedures and documenting anamnesis. Data-based process management and process control in order to time interventions optimally is not possible without real-time monitoring either. As displayed in Figure 14, the generic principles serve as decision guidelines for process management and adaptive indication. In the future, process monitoring will also become more relevant in supporting clients after their discharge as well as in feedback-supported Internet therapies.

9.2 Evidence-Based Practice and Relative Rational Justification of Treatments

A further consequence is the conception of *evidence-based decisions*. In an extended systemic understanding, this implies that therapeutical procedures and decisions (adaptive indications) can be justified relatively rationally with reference to theoretical models, empirical evidence, and the current status of the therapy system (i.e., the client, but also the therapist and the setting). This definition refers explicitly to Westmeyer's (1979, 1984, 1997) negotiation model, which makes it possible for several different references to come to a relative rational decision. These can be research results on interventions and therapeutic procedures,

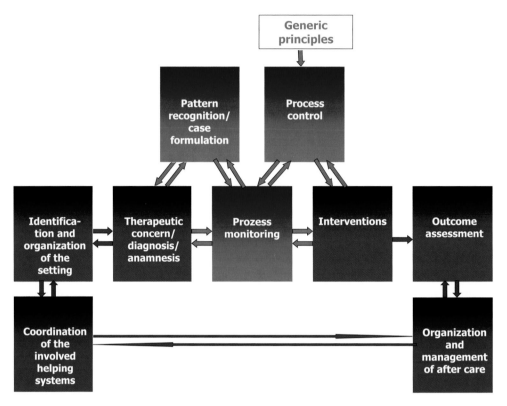

Figure 29

More commonly used steps and components of psychotherapy (blue fields) can be enhanced using process monitoring (red fields). This is central in an integrative psychotherapy concept, as it contributes process data to cross-sectional data and thus facilitates pattern recognition during the therapeutic change process and for purposes of case formulation. Only in this way can process dynamics (e.g., fluctuations in emotions) be uncovered; this in turn enables process control that is based on the generic principles to support processes of self-organization (see also Figure 14).

characteristics of the therapist, such as personal preferences and competencies, characteristics of the client, the setting, or the process.

As listed in the middle box of Figure 30, this understanding of evidence-based decisions can be equated with the use of different therapy methods that have been shown to be effective in randomized controlled trials. However, we have to keep the following restricting factors in mind: (a) interventions only explain a small fraction of the outcome variance of therapies and (b) nonlinear systems cannot be controlled using standardized input and predicted linear effects. Furthermore, (c) to allot therapy programs to groups of mental dysfunctions (that are evidenced in controlled studies) takes place on a medium level: dysfunction groups (or diagnosis groups) are assigned to probabilities for effects to occur in relation to treatment types and in relation to the operationalizations chosen in the respective studies. This categorization provides only a small amount of information about the need for treatment in individual cases and individual dynamics. In Figure 30, this level is called *RCT evidence*.

A relative rational justification of therapeutic decisions should always correspond to the current state of the individual dynamic of the attended system. Interventions should be per-

| **Nomothetics** |
| Clinical justification is related to and based on theories of learning, development, and dynamic complex systems |
| **Nomothetic evidence** |

| **RCT-based evidence** |
| Clinical justification is related to nosological classification (diagnoses) and related types of interventions/techniques |
| **Evidence based on randomized controlled trials** |

| **Idiographics** |
| Assessment of structural, functional, and dynamic patterns of the single case is focused on the individual client (humanism) |
| **Idiographic evidence** |

Figure 30

"Relative rational justification" of clinical action: Three justification levels of the therapeutic procedure embedded in an extended concept of evidence-based psychotherapy.

formed or be refrained from according to the latest process data. This type of justification, which is oriented on single case data, is called *idiographic evidence*.

In order to make these decisions soundly, we need not only the availablitiy of process data, but also decision rules. These rules need to be based on a clear theoretical framework, which should be given by a general empirical model of change processes. Assuming that psychotherapy takes place on the level of the involved neuronal, mental, and social systems in the form of nonlinear and nonstationary dynamics, synergetics – as general theory of self-organized pattern changes – and the generic principles as decision rules adopt a prominent role here (see Figures 14 and 29). This level of theory-based reference of therapy decisions is called *nomothetic evidence*.

The classical definition of evidence-based practice is thus amended by two crucial levels – idiographic and nomothetic. Above all, evidence for a possible effectiveness is no longer assigned context-independently or to interventions or treatement programs per se, but instead has to be justified, empirically (that is data-based) supported, and revised when required in each individual case, that is *context-dependent*. So, "evidence-based" is not an attribute of events (e.g., the treatments offered) in the system's environment, but a system-relative qualification of the therapeutic procedure.

Above all, the "evidence" for a (possible) effectiveness is not assigned without context according to the intervention or the treatment program per se, but be substantiated empirically, i.e., based on data.

9.3 The Relation Between Common Factors and Generic Principles

We identify a close correspondence between many of the psychotherapy efficacy factors discussed in the literature (Duncan et al., 2010; Orlinsky et al., 1994, 2004) and the generic priniciples of self-organizing processes (Chapter 4). This relation is discussed exhaustively in Haken and Schiepek (2010, pp. 446–455). In this way, the importance of the therapeutical relationship for a positive therapy outcome can be related to principles 1 and 6. The therapist fundamentally conveys emotional safety and trust; a stress-free relationship between client and therapist facilitates self-reflection and learning without cortical inhibition. In the best case, this is much more than just stable boundary conditions but a relationship and attachment system that makes it possible to establish new emotionally relevant and corrective relationship experience. At this point, Priniciple 6 becomes relevant, which underlines the communicative, emotional, and cognitive resonance and synchronization between the changing system (client, couple, or family) and the therapist. Such resonance processes are a condition and a medium for social learning; that is, intrasystemic function changes that ultimately lead to cognitive and emotional changes in structure (a process to be described at the level of neuronal plasticity).

It is easy to intervene or unsettle self-organizing systems that are verging on instability, yet very difficult to do so when they are in a stable state. This is the reason why interventions and therapy techniques contribute only slightly to the therapy result (see Section 2.1) and why different therapy approaches show very similar levels of effectivness (see Section 2.3). This characteristic of self-organizing systems is, in turn, mediated by the occurrence and degree of the respective control parameters (e.g., the intrinsic motivation for change). In instable states, even small impulses – be it minimal interventions or random events – can lead to a transition into new states. Sometimes even system-internal flucutations (e.g., appearance of inner images) can be sufficient. This is why very diverse interventions can be successful and effective, provided they match the concept and comprehension models (generic principle 3) and the dynamics of the inner processes of the client (generic principle 6). Figure 31 illustrates these relations.

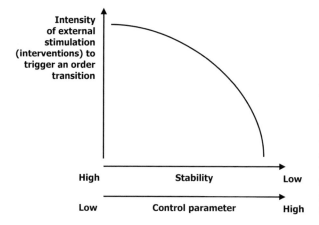

Figure 31
Relation between control parameter value(s), stability of the present order state (both displayed on the x-axis) and the value of external interventions that is necessary to trigger an order transition (y-axis). Reproduced with permission from Haken, H., & Schiepek, G. (2010), *Synergetik in der Psychologie: Selbstorganisation verstehen und gestalten* [Synergetics of psychology: Understanding and facilitating self-organization] (2nd ed.), p. 175. © Hogrefe.

It is immediately plausible that the sudden changes description in Section 2.5 can be interpreted as order transitions (phase transition-like phenomena). And this is not simply because the phenomena – as repeatedly identified in the relevant literature – are discontinuous and evidently not related to specific inputs, but also because of the associated critical instabilities of the system dynamics. The latter is almost never mentioned in the literature as a connection to the theory of self-organization is rarely established in the mainstream and the data basis (highly frequent process measurements) is often missing. However, where both are existent, critical instabilities can easily be identified in temporal proximity of order changes. Heinzel et al. (2014) used the SNS in the outpatient treatment of 18 patients with obsessive-compulsive disorder and found that spontaneous symptom reduction (measured twice weekly using the Yale-Brown Obsessive Compulsive Scale, Goodman et al., 1989) occurred *before* the main intervention of the behavioral therapy treatment (exposure to obsession-triggering objects and situations with response prevention, green bar in Figure 32). In temporal proximity of this transition, many items of the TPQ showed critical instabilities; that is, temporary significant increases of the dynamic complexity of these items (see also the results in Haken & Schiepek, 2010, Chapter 5; Schiepek et al., 2009, 2014).

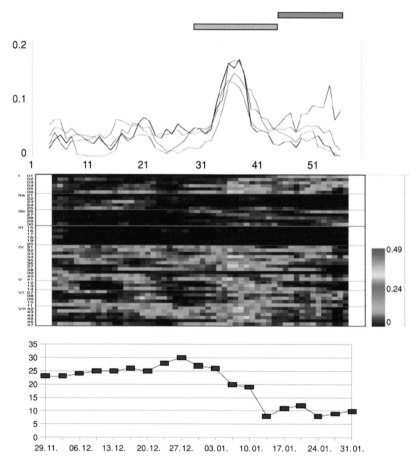

Figure 32
Example of an order transition during the therapy of a patient with obsessive-compulsive disorder (subtype: washing/contamination fear) (64 days correspond to 64 measurements). Top row: Pink bar: Critical instability (statistically significant dynamic complexity values). Green bar: Period of exposure with response prevention. Curves: Dynamic complexity of the TPQ factors I "therapeutic progress/confidence/self-efficacy" (blue), IV "dysphoric affectivity/self-relatedness" (red), V "broadening in perspective and innovation" (green), and VII "discomfort and pressure" (black). Middle row: The corresponding complexity resonance diagram, where the dynamic complexity values are color-coded. Yellow, orange, and red tones connote high complexity. Bottom row: The diagram shows the course of the Y-BOCS, with considerably decreased values in proximity to critical instability already before the onset of the exposure phase.

9.4 The Model of Self-Organization as a Synthesis of the Medical Model and the Common Factors Model

The proposed concept of psychotherapy as feedback-aided support of processes of self-organization could provide a synthesis of the classical dichotomy between the medical model and the common factors model (Wampold, 2010). The medical model assumes that any problem (disorder, disease) has a specific (mostly biological, but also psychological) reason with a corresponding inferable therapeutical method of action. This, in turn, implies certain approaches that cause therapeutic effects in a targeted way; from this point of view, other aspects, such as the therapeutic relationship, are not (or only marginally) responsible. These assumptions – based on a linear-causal input-output mechanism (or cause-effect mechanism or treatment-effect mechanism) – do not only dominate in medicine, but also in clinical psychology. We can therefore call the medical model the "standard model" (Schiepek, 2009). In contrast, the *common factors model* emphasizes the cooperation and interaction of client and therapist as well as their personalities, and it focuses more on the structure of the therapeutic work and the way it is transported or made plausible to the client than on the specific contents and techniques of the approach (Wampold, 2010). The psychotherapy model of self-organization is more consistent with the common factors model, not least because many of the common factors can be subsumed to the generic principles of SPM, as identified above.

These two models could prove integratable if patterns and structures relevant for changes find systemic explanations as dysfunctional processes of self-organization or as structural 'condensates' of such processes, or if changes can be explained systemically and triggered by feedback – in the sense of providing conditions for therapeutic self-organization.

Some particular models of self-organization do correspond to the criteria of the medical model; for example, the model of adaptive neuromodulation (see Section 10.1.2) that looks into the details of the system processes, concerning both pathogenetic mechanisms (see Tass et al., 2010, for the Parkinsonian tremor example) and therapy (Tass, 2003; Tass & Hauptmann, 2007; Tass & Popovych, 2012). However, this model does not feature a linear input-output mechanism, but instead provides a mathematical description of the re-organization of dysfunctional (for instance over-synchronized) system structures, using principles of synergetics (in this case the 'inversion' of the slaving principle) and neuronal plasticity.

A *psychotherapy model of self-organization* implies that (a) therapy is providing support for processes of self-organization, that (b) unspecific factors thus become specific ones, because they become clearly theoretically classified (for example as generic principles), that (c) the assumption of input-output mechanisms is theoretically obsolete, and that (d) systemic processes of re-organization can be explained scientifically by models of complexity science and self-organization and supported explicitly (using process monitoring and feedback). It is thus possible to synthesize the medical model and the common factors model under the umbrella of the theory of self-organization. This is, of course, a topic for further discussion.

Chapter 10

Integrated Systemic Psychotherapy

In the first two chapters, we showed why a school-independent, integrative approach is meaningful for future psychotherapy. We tried to make clear that this is about more than just the integration of different therapy schools. It is about the integration of quantitative (explanative) and qualitative (understanding) approaches, and the integration of nomothetic (looking for general principles) and idiographic (single-case oriented) approaches in psychology. There is hardly a psychological theory that refers to single cases and their dynamics as clearly as the theory of nonlinear complex systems, especially chaos theory (Pincus, 2009; Strunk & Schiepek, 2006). It implies the paradox that, if its assumptions are valid

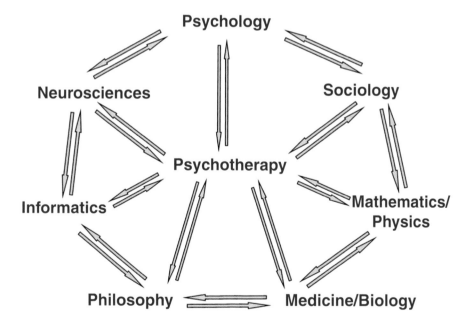

Figure 33
Psychotherapy at the intersection of different disciplines. For the connecting ties and meta-theoretical frame, including a transdisciplinary terminology, the theory of complex dynamic systems is used. The education and training in the scientist-practitioner model of psychotherapy is based on the concept of systems competence (i.e., competencies in understanding, modeling, analysis, and handling complex systems; Haken & Schiepek, 2010, p. 670ff.).

(e.g., nonlinearity; sensitive dependency on initial conditions and on minimal fluctuations or interventions; critical instability at symmetry breakings), the dynamics and system structures of individual cases have to become the focus of attention precisely because of these general (nomothetic) laws.

Furthermore, it should be clear by this point that psychotherapy is not only to be seen as applied psychology, but as interfacing several different disciplines (see Figure 33). Many different disciplines are involved, including information technology (e.g., when using internet-based procedures) as well as methods of linear and nonlinear time series analysis originating from physics and mathematics, but also psychology and sociology. The theoretical science of complex dynamic systems provides the meta-theoretical framework.

We predict that neuroscience will play a decisive role in this inter- and transdisciplinary ensemble in the future. Already today, we see some approaches of systemic neurotherapies that, in the future, could be further developed and even combined with talking, understanding, and experience-focused psychotherapy methods. Any attempt to define systemic therapy/ies should be aware of these systemic neurotherapies and should ensure that they are developed further with all intensity and that they are open for integration with psychotherapy. However, the reader should be aware that these approaches are not yet well established in psychiatric or psychosomatic fields of application. From the above, it follows that it would be more appropriate to talk about *systemic therapies* in the plural, as there are several systemic neurotherapies and possibly also several systemic psychotherapies. We will now present two neurotherapy approaches.

10.1 Systemic Neurotherapies

10.1.1 Real-Time Neuro-Feedback With fMRI

Powerful computers make it possible to analyze and format the BOLD signals of magnetic resonance imaging scanners (fMRI) with only a few seconds' delay. The signal measuring the differences in concentration of oxygenated blood in certain brain areas indirectly provides information about neuronal activity in these areas. This signal can be displayed via a computer-interface and fed back to the subject in the scanner as if it were in real-time (de Charms, 2008). Comparable to bio-feedback with peripheral-physiological or EEG signals (Rief & Birbaumer, 2006), clients can learn to control their neuronal activity this way, or even to coordinate it with the neuronal activity of another person (de Charms et al., 2004). The MRI allows for a relatively exact localization of changes in oxygen level of the brain perfusion and thus also of neuronal activity, even in deeper brain structures (e.g., basal ganglia, limbic areas), and this opens up far-reaching possibilities for neuromodulation (de Charms, 2008). Results are available from pain therapy (de Charms et al., 2005) and modulation of emotional structures; for instance, the anterior cingulate cortex (ACC) (Johnston et al., 2010). Applications in psychiatric disorders have also been tested (e.g., in schizophrenic patients; the study by Ruiz et al., 2011, examined the perception of emotions in facial expressions focusing on the insular cortex of the observer).

This technology is systemic because adding an external loop via the perception of internal processes (i.e., the neuronal activity) to the system-internal feedback loops of the brain facilitates self-regulation and self-organization without a direct intervention. In addition to the usual methods of activity modulation in specific brain areas, Ruiz et al. (2011) also test-ed the effects of real-time feedback on connectivity patterns and coupling strength *between* brain areas. In a manner of speaking, this is a systemic approach in two respects: on the one hand, it is directed towards the function of complex systems and, on the other hand, it interprets therapy as the realization of systemic feedback processes.

10.1.2 Neuromodulation

Several neurological and psychiatric disorders accompany specific patterns of synchro-nization (Siegel, Donner, & Engel, 2012) or a considerably increased, rhythm-dependent synchronization of brain areas and their respective neuronal populations (Schulman et al., 2011), which are processed independently in healthy physiological functioning. In healthy functioning they are able to synchronize and de-synchronize in a highly adaptive and flexi-ble manner. We find such over-synchronizations in epilepsy, Parkinsonian disease, essential tremor, or tinnitus (Tass & Hauptmann, 2007; Tass & Majtanik, 2006; Tass et al., 2010), and presumably also in obsessive-compulsive disorders, major depression, and personality disorders (for the involved brain areas and neuronal networks, see the respective articles in Schiepek, 2011, and other references: personality disorders, e.g., Buchheim, Roth, Schie-pek, Pogarell, & Karch, 2013; major depression, e.g., Drevets, Price, & Furey, 2008; Grei-cius et al., 2007; obsessive compulsive disorder, e.g., Menzies et al., 2008). In the past few years, Tass and colleagues have developed mathematical models that show how coupled nonlinear oscillators (Kuramoto, 1984; Osipov et al., 2007) can be desynchronized by *coor-dinated reset* (Tass, 2003) or *nonlinear delayed feedback* (Popovych, Hauptmann, & Tass, 2006). In simulations, it was possible to kindle as well as anti-kindle coupling processes (Tass & Majtanik, 2006). Thus, deep brain stimulation that usually works with high-fre-quency continuous stimulation (ca. 120 Hz), and by this simply suppresses neuronal activ-ity, can now be applied temporarily and on demand. This gentle treatment method showed long-term effects. In Parkinson, the rebound effect, which often occurs after high-frequency stimulation is completed, could be largely avoided.

   The method uses synergetic modeling in order to reverse established pathological orders and the accompanying slaving of subsystems (neuronal populations). In line with synerget-ics, simulations showed that a healthy, desynchronized attractor is already established when the system dynamics leaves the basin; that is, when it leaves the zone of attraction of the pathological attractor (oversynchronization) and passes the separatrix over to the basin of a physiologically adequate attractor (Figure 34). In doing so, the system reorganizes itself using the principles of self-organization. The establishment of new patterns also leads to new connections between the neurons involved and initiates a process of restructuring via shifts in the synaptic coupling strengths, which stabilizes the system to a physiologically healthy dynamics even without further stimulation through the implanted electrodes (Tass & Hauptmann, 2007).

   This, by itself, is already a huge gain for neurological disorders – particularly because of the precise systemic or synergetic models, respectively, that are the basis for these meth-ods of deep brain stimulation with coordinated reset and nonlinear delayed feedback. The fascinating perspective for treating mental illnesses is that a noninvasive de-synchronization therapy has been developed, which is based on the coordinated reset principle with acoustic or fibro-tactile stimulation. We now have a viable and – as documented in controlled studies

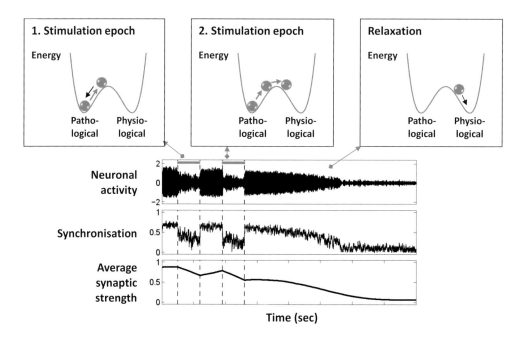

Figure 34

Top row: Displayed is the transition of the dynamics of a neuronal network from a pathological (over-synchronized) state to a physiologically healthy state. Bottom row: An over-synchronized neuronal system is stimulated using the coordinated reset method, reducing the coherence in neuronal activity. Degree of synchronization and strength of the synaptic connections change accordingly. However, the initial stimulation does not suffice to transform the system dynamics into a changed (physiological and healthy, respectively) attractor. Since synaptic strength is now reduced, the next stimulation phase pushes the system dynamics into a healthy attractor. The ball (system dynamics) in the top row exceeds the separatrix after the second stimulation and rolls down into a new valley (attractor). The neuronal system relaxes entirely by itself – that is, without further stimulation – into the new state. Figure reproduced with permission from Tass, P. A., & Hauptmann, C. (2007). Therapeutic modulation of synaptic connectivity with desynchronizing brain stimulation. *International Journal of Psychophysiology, 64*, 53–61.

– very effective (in this case: acoustic) treatment for tinnitus (Tass, Adamchic, Freund, von Stackelberg, & Hauptmann, 2012).

Real-time neurofeedback with fMRI and noninvasive neuromodulation combined with psychotherapy could create completely new perspectives for the therapy of mental health disorders in the future. Classical (i.e., experience-based psychological) psychotherapy could be prepared for, supplemented, or supported using these methods. Using process feedback systems can be seen as an essential characteristic of systemic therapies. They are all about changing dysfunctional patterns of complex neuronal or mental systems; or, in other words, about influencing processes of self-organization using feedback and stimulation methods. It can be concluded that all these are systemic therapies (that is, therapies focusing on the function and dynamics of complex systems) and that they could reach their full potential when combined.

10.2 Systemic Therapies

Against the background of these developments, we propose the following definition of systemic therapies:

> *Systemic therapy* in this understanding enables change processes of states of a system or network of systems (regarding structures and/or functions) that are considered dysfunctional or in deficit. In order to accomplish these changes, methods are used that can be placed in the theory spectrum of complex, dynamic, and nonlinear systems. An essential and integral part of therapy and change is the process measurement of the systems and their dynamics; that is, consequent process feedback. The therapy and change process itself is conceived and realized as a dynamic, self-organizing system.

Such an open definition of systemic therapies implies that
1. the focus of the treatment has systemic qualities (e.g., neuronal systems, mental structures, interpersonal systems) and can be modeled using system-theoretical methods;
2. no a priori constriction to a specific level of functioning (e.g., a biological, mental, or interpersonal-communicative level) is made;
3. systemic therapies are not limited to psychotherapy – neurobiological or biomedical treatments can just as well be systemic to this effect as can psychological or social ones; and that
4. no a priori constriction to particular interventions or therapy schools is made in the field of psychotherapy.

According to this definition, therapy involving families, couples or other constellations comprising more than one person is not sufficient to define the work as systemic. As well as this, these constellations have to be conceptualized and realized as dynamic systems. Regarding item 2, we wish to point out that, in everyday practice, it will rarely be possible to measure (neuro-)biological, intrapsychic, and social processes simultaneously and to conduct interventions at all these levels. Nevertheless, these levels have to be considered and it has to be justified in each case why the focus is placed on a specific system level.

According to this definition, systemic psychotherapy is an integrative concept of *psycho*therapy and a subset of systemic therapies in general. According to the concept of synergetic process management presented here, the characteristics of systemic psychotherapy are: (a) the reference to meta-theories from the spectrum of complex, dynamic systems, and synergetics in particular, (b) procedure justification using the generic principles, (c) an idiographic approach concerning case formulation and process monitoring, and (d) the use of therapy feedback and therapy regulation, in particular, by the means of making use of the SNS.

The proposal for an integrative – that is, a school- and discipline-independent therapy – developed in this volume, which follows Sigmund Freud's call for practice and research to be linked, should now be widened to include correspondent education and training concepts. A scientist-practitioner model is desirable. It will be interesting and rewarding to follow the discussions, specifications, elaborations, practical testing, and developments in this area over the next few years.

References

Ahn, H., & Wampold, B. E. (2001). Where oh where are the specific ingredients? A meta-analysis of component studies in counselling and psychotherapy. *Journal of Counseling Psychology, 48*, 251–257. http://doi.org/10.1037/0022-0167.48.3.251

Ambühl, H. R., & Mühlmann, T. (1991). Gefühlsbezogene therapeutische Interventionen, Aufnahmebereitschaft des Klienten und Postsession Outcome. Eine Einzelfallstudie [Feelings-oriented therapeutic interventions: Receptivity of the client and postsession outcome in a single case study]. *Schweizerische Zeitschrift für Psychologie, 50*, 248–259.

Anderson, H., & Goolishian, H. (1988). Human systems as linguistic systems: Preliminary and evolving ideas about the implications of clinical theory. *Family Process, 27*, 371–393. http://doi.org/10.1111/j.1545-5300.1988.00371.x

Anderson, T. (1999 June). *Specifying non-"specifics" in therapists: The effect of facilitative interpersonal skills in outcome and alliance formation.* Paper presented at the 30th annual meeting of the International Society of Psychotherapy Research, Braga, Portugal.

Anderson, T., Lunnen, K. M., & Ogles, B. M. (2010). Putting models and techniques in context. In B. Duncan, S. Miller, B. Wampold, & M. Hubble (Eds.), *The heart and soul of change* (2nd ed., pp. 143–166). Washington, DC: American Psychological Association.

Anker, M., Duncan, B., & Sparks, J. (2009). Using client feedback to improve couples therapy outcomes: A randomized clinical trial in a naturalistic setting. *Journal of Consulting and Clinical Psychology, 77*, 693–704. http://doi.org/10.1037/a0016062

Antonovsky, A. (1987). *Unraveling the mystery of health.* London, UK: Jossey Bass.

Antony, M. M., Bieling, P. J., Cox, B. J., Enns, M. W., & Swinson, R. P. (1998). Psychometric properties of the 42-item and 21-item versions of the Depression Anxiety and Stress Scales (DASS) in clinical groups and a community sample. *Psychological Assessment, 10*, 176–181. http://doi.org/10.1037/1040-3590.10.2.176

Asay, T. P., & Lambert, M. J. (1999). The empirical case for the common factors in therapy: Quantitative findings. In M. Hubble, B. Duncan, & S. Miller (Eds.), *The heart and soul of change: What works in therapy* (pp. 33–56). Washington, DC: American Psychological Association.

Atmanspacher, H., & Dalenoort, G. J. (1994). *Inside versus outside. Endo- and exo-concepts of observation and knowledge in physics, philosophy, and cognitive science.* Berlin, Germany: Springer.

Bandt, C., & Pompe, B. (2002). Permutation entropy: A natural complexity measure for time series. *Physical Review Letters, 88*, 174102 1–4. http://doi.org/10.1103/PhysRevLett.88.174102

Barak, A., Hen, L., Boniel-Nissim, M., & Shapira, N. (2008). A comprehensive review and a meta-analysis of the effectiveness of internet-based psychotherapeutic interventions. *Journal of Technology in Human Services, 26*, 109–160. http://doi.org/10.1080/15228830802094429

Barber, J. P., Crits-Christoph, P., & Luborsky, L. (1996). Effects of therapist adherence and competence on patient outcome in brief dynamic therapy. *Journal of Consulting and Clinical Psychology, 64*, 619–622. http://doi.org/10.1037/0022-006X.64.3.619

Baskin, T. W., Tierney, C. S., Minami, T., & Wampold, B. E. (2003). Establishing specificity in psychotherapy: A meta-analysis of structural equivalence of placebo controls. *Journal of Consulting and Clinical Psychology, 71*, 973–979. http://doi.org/10.1037/0022-006X.71.6.973

Bee, P., Bower, P., Lovell, K., Gilbody, S., Richards, D., Gask, L., & Roach, P. (2008). Psychotherapy mediated by remote communication technologies: A meta-analytic review. *BMC Psychiatry, 8(1)*, 60. http://doi.org/10.1186/1471-244X-8-60

Beirle, G., & Schiepek, G. (2002). Psychotherapie als Veränderung von Übergangsmustern zwischen "States of Mind." Einzelfallanalyse einer systemisch-ressourcenorientierten Kurzzeittherapie [Psychotherapy as change of transitionary patterns between "states of mind": Single case analysis of a systemic-resource-oriented short-term therapy]. *Psychotherapie, Psychosomatik und Medizinische Psychologie, 52*, 214–225. http://doi.org/10.1055/s-2001-28525

Benish, S., Imel, Z. E., & Wampold, B. E. (2008). The relative efficacy of bona fide psychotherapies of post-traumatic stress disorder: A meta-analysis of direct comparisons. *Clinical Psychology Review, 28*, 746–758. http://doi.org/10.1016/j.cpr.2008.06.001

Berg, I. K., & Miller, S. D. (1992). *Working with the problem drinker. Solution-focused approach*. New York, NY: Norton.

Berman, J. S., Miller, C., & Massman, P. J. (1985). Cognitive therapy versus systematic desensitization: Is one treatment superior? *Psychological Bulletin, 97*, 451–461. http://doi.org/10.1037/0033-2909.97.3.451

Bertalanffy, L. von (1968). *General system theory*. New York, NY: Braziller.

Beutler, L. E., Malik, M., Alimohamed, S., Harwood, T. M., Talebi, H., Noble, S., & Wong, E. (2004). Therapist variables. In M. J. Lambert (Ed.), *Bergin and Garfield's handbook of psychotherapy and behavior change* (pp. 227–306). New York, NY: Wiley.

Bohart, A. C., Elliott, R., Greenberg, L. S., & Watson, J. C. (2002). Empathy. In J. C. Norcross (Ed.), *Psychotherapy relationships that work* (pp. 89–108). New York, NY: Oxford University Press.

Bohart, A. C., & Tallman, K. (2010). Clients: The neglected common factor in psychotherapy. In B. Duncan, S. Miller, B. Wampold, & M. Hubble (Eds.), *The heart and soul of change* (2nd. ed., pp. 83–111). Washington, DC: American Psychological Association.

Bohus, M., Kleindienst, N., Limberger, M. F., Stieglitz, R. D., Domsalla, M., Chapman, A., … Wolf, M. (2009). The short-version of the Borderline Symptom List (BSL-23): Development and initial data on psychometric properties. *Psychopathology, 42*, 32–39. http://doi.org/10.1159/000173701

Bohus, M., Schmahl, C., & Mauchnik, J. (2011). Borderline-Persönlichkeitsstörungen [Borderline personality disorders]. In G. Schiepek (Ed.), *Neurobiologie der Psychotherapie* (2nd ed., pp. 433–449). Stuttgart, Germany: Schattauer.

Bowlby, J. (1973). *Attachment and loss. Vol. 2: Separation, anxiety, and anger*. London: Hogarth Press.

Bowlby, J. (1980). *Attachment and loss. Vol. 3: Loss*. New York, NY: Basic Books.

Brockmann, J., & Sammet, I. (2003). Die Control Mastery Theorie von Weiss [Weiss' control mastery]. In A. Gerlach, A. M. Schlösser, & A. Springer (Eds.), *Psychoanalyse mit und ohne Couch* (pp. 280–293). Bonn, Germany: Psychosozial-Verlag.

Bruder-Bezzel, A. (1991). *Die Geschichte der Individualpsychologie* [The history of individual psychology]. Frankfurt am Main, Germany: Fischer.

Bruder-Bezzel, A. (Ed.) (2009). *Alfred-Adler-Studienausgabe, Band 7: Gesellschaft und Kultur (1897–1937)* [Alfred Adler student's edition, Vol. 7: Society and culture]. Göttingen, Germany: Vandenhoeck & Ruprecht.

Buchheim, A., Roth, G., Schiepek, G., Pogarell, O., & Karch, S. (2013). Neurobiology of personality disorder (BPD) and antisocial personality disorder (APD). *Swiss Archives of Neurology and Psychiatry, 164*, 115–122.

Busch, A., Kanter, J. Landes, S., & Kohlenberg, R. (2006). Sudden gains and outcome: A broader temporal analysis of cognitive therapy for depression. *Behaviour Therapy, 37*, 61–68. http://doi.org/10.1016/j.beth.2005.04.002

Carter, C., Sue, I., Lederhendler, I., & Kirkpatrick, B. (1997). *The integrative neurobiology of affiliation*. New York, NY: Academy of Science.

Caspar, F. (1996). *Beziehungen und Probleme verstehen. Eine Einführung in die psychotherapeutische Plananalyse* [Understanding relationships and problems. An introduction to psychotherapeutic plan anaysis] (2nd ed.). Bern, Switzerland: Huber.

Castonguay, L. G., Goldfried, M. R., Wiser, S., Raue, P. J., & Hayes, A. M. (1996). Predicting the effect of cognitive therapy for depression: A study of unique and common factors. *Journal of Consulting and Clinical Psychology, 64*, 497–504. http://doi.org/10.1037/0022-006X.64.3.497

Castonguay, L. G., & Hill, C. E. (Eds.). (2012). *Transformation in psychotherapy: Corrective experiences across cognitive behavioral, humanistic, and psychodynamic approaches*. Washington, DC: American Psychological Association.

Christensen, A., & Heavey, C. L. (1999). Interventions for couples. *Annual Review of Psychology, 50*, 165–190. http://doi.org/10.1146/annurev.psych.50.1.165

Cierpka, M. (Ed.) (2008). *Handbuch der Familiendiagnostik* [Handbook of family diagnostic]. Heidelberg & Berlin, Germany: Springer. http://doi.org/10.1007/978-3-540-78475-3

Ciompi, L. (1997). *Die emotionalen Grundlagen des Denkens. Entwurf einer fraktalen Affektlogik* [The emotional basis of thinking. Outline of a fractal affect logic]. Göttingen, Germany: Vandenhoeck & Ruprecht.

Clarkin, J. F., & Levy, K. N. (2004). The influence of client variables on psychotherapy. In M. J. Lambert (Ed.), *Bergin and Garfield's handbook of psychotherapy and behavior change* (pp. 194–226). New York, NY: Wiley.

Cohen, L. (1989). Time-frequency distributions – a review. *Proc IEEE, 77*, 941–981.

Cooper, J., & Axsom, D. (1982). Effort justification in psychotherapy. In G. Weary & H. L. Mirels (Eds.), *Integrations of clinical and social psychology* (pp. 214–230). New York, NY: Oxford University Press.

Cousins, N. (1980). *Anatomy of an illness*. New York: W. W. Norton.

Crits-Christoph, P., Gibbons, M. B., Hamilton, J., Ring-Kurtz, S., & Gallop, R. (2011). The dependability of alliance assessments: The alliance-outcome correlation is larger than you might think. *Journal of Consulting and Clinical Psychology, 79*, 267–278. http://doi.org/10.1037/a0023668

Cummings, A. L., Hallberg, E., Slemon, A., & Martin, J. (1992). Participants' memories for therapeutic events and ratings of session effectiveness. *Journal of Cognitive Psychotherapy, 6*, 113–124.

Curtis, J., & Silberschatz, G. (1996). Strukturierte psychodynamische Fallkonzeptionen: Der Mt. Zion Ansatz [Structured psychodynamic case formulation: The Mount Zion approach]. In F. Caspar (Ed.), *Psychotherapeutische Problemanalyse* (S. 303–313). Tübingen: DGVT.

Dalter, W., Gstach, J., & Wininger, M. (Ed.). (2009). *Alfred-Adler-Studienausgabe, Band 4: Erziehung und Erziehungsberatung (1913–1937)* [Alfred Adler student's edition, Vol. 4: Education and educational counseling]. Göttingen, Germany: Vandenhoeck & Ruprecht.

Davidson, M. (1983). *Uncommon sense*. Los Angeles, CA: Tarcher.

de Charms, R. C. (2008). Applications of real-time fMRI. *Nature Revue Neuroscience, 9*, 720–729. http://doi.org/10.1038/nrn2414

de Charms, R. C., Christoff, K., Glover, G. H., Pauly, J. M., Whitfield, S., & Gabrieli, J. D. (2004). Learned regulation of spatially localized brain activation using real-time fMRI. *NeuroImage, 21*, 436–443. http://doi.org/10.1016/j.neuroimage.2003.08.041

de Charms, R. C., Maeda, F., Glover, G. H., Ludlow, D., Pauly, J. M., Soneji, D., … Mackey, S. C. (2005). Control over brain activation and pain learned by using real-time functional MRI. *Proceedings of the National Academy of Sciences USA, 102*, 18626–18631. http://doi.org/10.1073/pnas.0505210102

Deco, G., Jirsa, V. K., & McIntosh, A. R. (2010). Emerging concepts for the dynamical organization of resting-state activity in the brain. *Nature Review Neuroscience, 12*, 43–56. http://doi.org/10.1038/nrn2961

Deco, G., Jirsa, V. K., & McIntosh, A. R. (2013). Resting brains never rest: Computational insights into potential cognitive architectures. *Trends in Neuroscience, 36*, 268–274. http://doi.org/10.1016/j.tins.2013.03.001

de Shazer, S. (1985). *Keys to solution in brief therapy*. New York, NY: Norton.

Drevets, W. C., Price, J. L., & Furey, M. L. (2008). Brain structural and functional abnormalities in mood disorders: Implications for neurocircuitry models of depression. *Brain Structure and Function, 213*, 93–118. http://doi.org/10.1007/s00429-008-0189-x

Duncan, B., Miller, S., & Sparks, J. A. (Eds.). (2004). *The heroic client: A revolutionary way to improve effectiveness through client-directed, outcome-informed therapy*. San Francisco, CA: Jossey-Bass.

Duncan, B., Miller, S., Wampold, B., & Hubble, M. (Eds.). (2010). *The heart and soul of change* (2nd ed.). Washington, DC: American Psychological Association.

Dunn, R. L., & Schwebel, A. I. (1995). Meta-analytic review of marital therapy outcome research. *Journal of Family Psychology, 9*, 58–68. http://doi.org/10.1037/0893-3200.9.1.58

Dush, D. M., Hirt, M. L., & Schroeder, H. (1983). Self-statement modification with adults: A meta-analysis. *Psychological Bulletin, 94*, 408–422. http://doi.org/10.1037/0033-2909.94.3.408

Ebner-Priemer, U.W., & Bohus, M. (2008). Elektronische Tagebücher in der Medizin: Echtzeiterfassung von Symptomen [Electronic diaries in medicine: Capturing symtpoms in real-time]. *Deutsches Ärzteblatt, 105*, 1550–1553

Ebner-Priemer, U., & Trull, T. (2009). Ecological momentary assessment of mood disorders and mood dysregulation. *Psychological Assessment, 21*, 463–475. http://doi.org/10.1037/a0017075

Eckmann, J. P., Oliffson Kamphorst, S., & Ruelle, D. (1987). Recurrence plots of dynamical systems. *Europhysics Letters, 4*, 973–977. http://doi.org/10.1209/0295-5075/4/9/004

Eliott, R., & James, E. (1989). Varieties of client experience in psychotherapy: An analysis of the literature. *Clinical Psychology Review, 9*, 443–467. http://doi.org/10.1016/0272-7358(89)90003-2

Fahrenberg, J., & Myrtek, M. (Eds.). (1996). *Ambulatory assessment: Computer-assisted psychological and psychophysiological methods in monitoring and field studies*. Cambridge, MA: Hogrefe Publishers.

Fahrenberg, J., Myrtek, M., Pawlik, K., & Perrez, M. (2007). Ambulatory assessmen: Monitoring behavior in daily life settings. *European Journal of Psychological Assessment, 23*, 206–213. http://doi.org/10.1027/1015-5759.23.4.206

Flatten, G. (2011). Posttraumatische Belastungsstörungen [Posttraumatic stress disorders]. In G. Schiepek (Ed.), *Neurobiologie der Psychotherapie* (2nd ed., pp. 450–471). Stuttgart, Germany: Schattauer.

Fornaro, P. (2009). *Funktion und Wirkung von therapeutischen Fragen im Prozess systemischer Paartherapie* [Function and effect of therapeutic questions in the process of systemic couple therapy]. (Diploma dissertation) Ludwig Maximilians University Munich, Germany.

Gaffan, E. A., Tsaousis, I., & Kemp-Wheeler, S. M. (1995). Researcher allegiance and meta-analysis: The case of cognitive therapy for depression. *Journal of Consulting and Clinical Psychology, 63*, 966–980. http://doi.org/10.1037/0022-006X.63.6.966

Garfield, S. L. (1992). Eclectic psychotherapy: A common factors approach. In J. C. Norcross & M. R. Goldfried (Eds.), *Handbook of psychotherapy integration* (pp. 169–201). New York, NY: Basic Books.

Garfield, S. L. (1994). Research on client variables in psychotherapy. In A. E. Bergin & S. L. Garfield (Eds.), *Handbook of psychotherapy and behavior change* (4th ed., pp. 191–228). New York, NY: Wiley.

Garfield, S. L. (1995). *Psychotherapy: An eclectic-integrative approach.* New York, NY: Wiley.

Gerstner, W., Kempter, R., van Hemmen, J., & Wagner, H. (1996). A neuronal learning rule for sub-millisecond temporal coding. *Nature, 383*, 76–81. http://doi.org/10.1038/383076a0

Globus, G. G., & Arpaia, J. P. (1994). Psychiatry and the new dynamics. *Biological Psychiatry, 35*, 352–364. http://doi.org/10.1016/0006-3223(94)90039-6

Goodman, W. K., Price, L. H., Rasmussen, S. A., Mazure, C., Fleischmann, R. L., Hill, C. L., … Charney, D. S. (1989). The Yale-Brown obsessive compulsive scale. I. Development, use, and reliability. *Archives of General Psychiatry, 46*, 1006–1011. http://doi.org/10.1001/archpsyc.1989.01810110048007

Grawe, K. (1995). Grundriss einer Allgemeinen Psychotherapie [Outline of a general psychotherapy]. *Psychotherapeut, 40*, 130–145.

Grawe, K. (2004a). *Psychological Therapy.* Cambridge, MA: Hogrefe & Huber Publishers.

Grawe, K. (2004b). *Neuropsychotherapie* [Neuropsychotherapy]. Göttingen, Germany: Hogrefe.

Grawe, K., Donati, R., & Bernauer, F. (1994). *Psychotherapie im Wandel. Von der Konfession zur Profession* [The evolution of psychotherapy: From confession to profession]. Göttingen, Germany: Hogrefe.

Grawe, K., Grawe-Gerber, M., Heininger, B., Ambühl, H., & Caspar, F. (1996). Schematheoretische Fallkonzeption und Therapieplanung: Eine Anleitung für Therapeuten [Schema-theoretical case formulation and therapy planning: An introduction for therapists]. In F. Caspar (Ed.), *Psychotherapeutische Problemanalyse* (pp. 189–224). Tübingen, Germany: DGVT.

Gregory, R. J., Canning, S. E., Lee, T. W., & Wise, J. C. (2004). Cognitive bibliotherapy for depression: A meta-analysis. *Professional Psychology: Research and Practice, 35*, 275–280. http://doi.org/10.1037/0735-7028.35.3.275

Greicius, M. D., Flores, B. H., Menon, V., Glover, G. H., Solvason, H. B., Kenna, H., … Schatzberg, A.F. (2007). Resting-state functional connectivity in major depression: Abnormally increased contributions from subgenual cingulate cortex and thalamus. *Biological Psychiatry, 62*, 429–437. http://doi.org/10.1016/j.biopsych.2006.09.020

Grencavage, L. M., & Norcross, J. C. (1990). Where are the commonalities among the therapeutic common factors? *Professional Psychology: Research and Practice, 21*, 372–378. http://doi.org/10.1037/0735-7028.21.5.372

Greve, N., & Keller, T. (Ed.) (2010). *Systemische Praxis in der Psychiatrie* [Systemic practice in psychiatry]. Heidelberg, Germany: Carl Auer.

Grosse Holtforth, M., & Grawe, K. (2004). Inkongruenz und Fallkonzeption in der Psychologischen Therapie [Incongruence and case formulation in psychological therapy]. *Verhaltenstherapie & psychosoziale Praxis, 36*, 9–21.

Gumz, A., Bauer, K., & Brähler, E. (2012). Corresponding instability of patient and therapist process ratings in psychodynamic psychotherapies. *Psychotherapy Research, 22*, 26–39. http://doi.org/10.1080/10503307.2011.622313

Gumz, A., Brähler, E., Geyer, M., & Erices, R. (2012). Crisis-repair sequences: Considerations on the classification and assessment of breaches in the therapeutic relationship. *BMC Medical Research Methodology, 12*, 10. http://doi.org/10.1186/1471-2288-12-10

Gunzelmann, T., Schiepek, G., & Reinecker, H. (1987). Laienhelfer in der psychosozialen Versorgung: Meta-Analysen zur differentiellen Effektivität von Laien und professionellen Helfern [Lay persons in psychosocial care: Meta-analyses on the differing effectivneess of lay and professional carers]. *Gruppendynamik, 18*, 361–384.

Gurin, J. (1990, March). Remaking our lives. *American Health*, 50–52.

Hahlweg, K., Dose, M., Dürr, H., & Müller, U. (2006). *Psychoedukative Familienbetreuung bei schizophrenen Patienten. Ein verhaltenstherapeutischer Ansatz zur Rückfallprophylaxe. Konzepte, Behandlungsanleitungen und Materialien* [Psychoeducative family care of patients with schizophrenia. A behavior therapy approach as relapse prophylaxis. Concepts, treatment guidelines, and materials]. (2nd ed.). Göttingen, Germany: Hogrefe.

Hahlweg, K., & Weidemann, G. (1999). Principles and results of family therapy in schizophrenia. *European Archives in Psychiatry and Clinical Neuroscience, 249* (Suppl. 4), 108–115. http://doi.org/10.1007/PL00014179

Haken, H. (1990). Synergetics as a tool for the conceptualization and mathematization of cognition and behavior – how far can we go? In H. Haken & M. Stadler (Eds.), *Synergetics of cognition* (pp. 2–31). Berlin, Germany: Springer. http://doi.org/10.1007/978-3-642-48779-8

Haken, H. (1996). *Principles of brain functioning. A synergetic approach to brain activity, behavior, and cognition*. Berlin, Germany: Springer.

Haken, H. (2002). *Brain dynamics*. Berlin, Germany: Springer.

Haken, H. (2004). *Synergetics. Introduction and advanced topics*. Berlin, Germany: Springer.

Haken, H. (2011). Synergetik der Gehirnfunktionen [The synergetics of brain functioning]. In G. Schiepek (Ed.), *Neurobiologie der Psychotherapie* (2nd ed., pp. 175–192). Stuttgart, Germany: Schattauer.

Haken, H., & Schiepek, G. (2010). *Synergetik in der Psychologie. Selbstorganisation verstehen und gestalten* [Synergetics in psychology. Understanding and facilitating self-organization] (2nd ed.). Göttingen, Germany: Hogrefe.

Hansch, D. (1997). *Psychosynergetik. Die fraktale Evolution des Psychischen. Grundlagen einer Allgemeinen Psychotherapie* [Psychosynergetics. The fractal evolution of the psyche]. Opladen, Germany: Westdeutscher Verlag.

Hartung, J. (1990). *Psychotherapie phobischer Störungen. Zur Handlungs- und Lageorientierung im Therapieprozess* [Psychotherapy of phobic disorders]. Wiesbaden, Germany: Deutscher Universitäts Verlag. http://doi.org/10.1007/978-3-322-90044-9

Hattie, J. A., Sharpley, C. F., & Rogers, H. F. (1984). Comparative effectiveness of professional and paraprofessional helpers. *Psychological Bulletin, 95*, 534–541. http://doi.org/10.1037/0033-2909.95.3.534

Hayes, A. M., Feldman, G. C., Beevers, C. G., Laurenceau, J. P., Cardaciotto, L. A., & Lewis-Smith, J. (2007). Discontinuities and cognitive changes in an exposure-based cognitive therapy for depression. *Journal of Consulting and Clinical Psychology, 75*, 409–421. http://doi.org/10.1037/0022-006X.75.3.409

Hayes, A. M., Laurenceau, J. P., Feldman, G. C., Strauss, J. L., & Cardaciotto, L. A. (2007). Change is not always linear: The study of nonlinear and discontinuous patterns of change in psychotherapy. *Clinical Psychology Review, 27*, 715 –723. http://doi.org/10.1016/j.cpr.2007.01.008

Hedges, L. V., & Olkin, I. (1985). *Statistical methods for meta-analysis*. San Diego, CA: Academic Press.

Hein, J. (2012). Analyse (in)direkter Effekte von Coaching anhand der generischen Prinzipien – eine empirische Fallstudie [Analysis of (in)direct effects of coaching following the generic principles – an empirical case study]. In C. Schiersmann & H. U. Thiel (Ed.), *Beratung als Förderung von Selbstorganisationsprozessen* (pp. 132–163). Göttingen, Germany: Vandenhoeck & Ruprecht.

Heinrichs, N., Bodenmann, G., & Hahlweg, K. (2008). *Prävention bei Paaren und Familien* [Prevention with couples and families]. Göttingen, Germany: Hogrefe.

Heinzel, S., Tominschek, I., & Schiepek, G. (2014). Dynamic patterns in psychotherapy – discontinuous changes and critical instabilities during the treatment of obsessive-compulsive disorder. *Nonlinear Dynamics, Psychology, and the Life Sciences, 18*, 155–176.

Henry, W. P., Schacht, T. E., Strupp, H. H., Butler, S. F., & Binder, J. (1993a). Effects of training in time-limited dynamic psychotherapy: Mediators of therapists' responses to training. *Journal of Consulting and Clinical Psychology, 61*, 441–447. http://doi.org/10.1037/0022-006X.61.3.434

Henry, W. P., Strupp, H. H., Butler, S. F., Schacht, T. E., & Binder, J. (1993b). Effects of training in time-limited dynamic psychotherapy: Changes in therapists' behavior. *Journal of Consulting and Clinical Psychology, 61*, 434–440. http://doi.org/10.1037/0022-006X.61.3.434

Horowitz, M. J. (1987). *States of mind*. New York, NY: Plenum Press. http://doi.org/10.1007/978-1-4899-7087-9

Horvath, A. O., & Symonds, B. D. (1991). Relation between working alliance and outcome in psychotherapy: A meta-analysis. *Journal of Counseling Psychology, 38*, 139–149. http://doi.org/10.1037/0022-0167.38.2.139

Ilardi, S. S., & Craighead, W. E. (1994). The role of non-specific factors in cognitive-behavior therapy for depression. *Clinical Psychology: Research and Practice, 1*, 138–156.

Ilardi, S. S., & Craighead, W. E. (1999). Rapid early response, cognitive modification, and nonspecific factors in cognitive-behavior therapy for depression: A reply to Tang and DeRubeis. *Clinical Psychology: Science and Practice, 6*, 295–299.

Johnston, S. J., Boehm, S. G., Healy, D., Goebel, R., & Linden, D. E. (2010). Neurofeedback: A promising tool for the self-regulation of emotion networks. *NeuroImage, 30*, 1066–1072. http://doi.org/10.1016/j.neuroimage.2009.07.056

Kanfer, F. H., Reinecker, H., & Schmelzer, D. (2006). *Selbstmanagement-Therapie* [Self-management therapy]. Berlin, Germany: Springer.

Kelly, M., Cyranowski, J., & Frank, E. (2007). Sudden gains in interpersonal psychotherapy for depression. *Behaviour Research and Therapy, 45*, 2563–2572. http://doi.org/10.1016/j.brat.2007.07.007

Kelly, M., Roberts, J., & Bottonari, K. (2007). Non-treatment-related sudden gains in depression: The role of self-evaluation. *Behaviour Research and Therapy, 45*, 737–747. http://doi.org/10.1016/j.brat.2006.06.008

Kelly, M., Roberts, J., & Ciesla, J. (2005). Sudden gains in cognitive behavioral treatment for depression: When do they occur and do they matter? *Behaviour Research and Therapy, 43*, 703–714. http://doi.org/10.1016/j.brat.2004.06.002

Kelso, J. A. S. (1995). *Dynamic patterns. The self-organization of brain and behavior.* Cambridge, MA: MIT Press.

Keupp, H. (1997). *Ermutigung zum aufrechten Gang* [Encouragement to stand tall]. Tübingen, Germany: DGVT-Verlag.

Knävelsrud, C., & Maercker, A. (2007). Internet-based treatment for PTSD reduces distress and facilitates the development of a strong therapeutic alliance: A randomized controlled clinical trial. *BMC Psychiatry, 7*, 13. http://doi.org/10.1186/1471-244X-7-13

Knuf, A., & Seibert, U. (Ed.) (2009). *Selbstbefähigung fördern. Empowerment und psychiatrische Arbeit* [Facilitating self-management: Empowerment and psychiatric work]. Bonn, Germany: Psychiatrie-Verlag.

Kowalik, Z. J., Schiepek, G., Kumpf, K., Roberts, L. E., & Elbert, T. (1997). Psychotherapy as a chaotic process II: The application of nonlinear analysis methods on quasi time series of the client–therapist interaction: A nonstationary approach. *Psychotherapy Research, 7*, 197–218. http://doi.org/10.1080/10503309712331331973

Kriz, J. (1990). Pragmatik systemischer Therapie-Theorie, Teil II: Der Mensch als Bezugspunkt systemischer Perspektiven [Pragmatic of systemic therapy theory, Part II: The person as reference point of systemic perspectives]. *System Familie, 3*, 97–107.

Kriz, J. (2004). Personenzentrierte Systemtheorie – Grundfragen und Kernaspekte [Person-centered system theory – basic questions and core aspects]. In A. von Schlippe & W. C. Kriz (Ed.), *Personzentrierung und Systemtheorie* (pp. 13–67). Göttingen, Germany: Vandenhoeck & Ruprecht.

Kriz, J. (2010). Systemtheorie als eine Metatheorie zur Integration psychotherapeutischer Ansätze [System theory as a meta-theory for the integration of psychotherapeutic approaches]. *Psychotherapie im Dialog, 11*, 28–33. http://doi.org/10.1055/s-0029-1223489

Kröger, B. (2013). *Hermann Haken und die Anfangsjahre der Synergetik* [Hermann Haken and the early years of synergetics]. Berlin, Germany: Logos.

Kuramoto, Y. (1984). *Chemical oscillations, waves, and turbulence.* Berlin, Germany: Springer. http://doi.org/10.1007/978-3-642-69689-3

Lambert, M. J. (1992). Psychotherapy outcome research: Implications for integrative and eclectic therapists. In J. C. Norcross & M. R. Goldfried (Eds.), *Handbook of psychotherapy integration* (pp. 94–129). New York, NY: Basic Books.

Lambert, M. J. (Ed.) (2004). *Bergin and Garfield's handbook of psychotherapy and behavior change.* New York, NY: Wiley.

Lambert, M. J. (2010). "Yes, it is time for clinicians to routinely monitor treatment outcome." In B. Duncan, S. Miller, B. Wampold, & M. Hubble (Eds.), *The heart and soul of change* (2nd. ed., pp. 237–266). Washington, DC: American Psychological Association.

Lambert, M. J. (2013). The efficacy and effectiveness of psychotherapy. In M. J. Lambert (Ed.), *Bergin and Garfield's handbook of psychotherapy and behavior change* (6th ed., pp. 169–218). New York, NY: Wiley.

Lambert, M. J., Harmon, C., Slade, K., Whipple, J. L., & Hawkins, E. J. (2005). Providing feedback to psychotherapists on their patient's progress: Clinical results and practice suggestions. *Journal of Clinical Psychology, 61*, 165–174. http://doi.org/10.1002/jclp.20113

Lambert, M. J., Morton, J. J., Hatfield, D. R., Harmon, C., Hamilton, S., & Shimokawa, K. (2004). *Administration and scoring manual for the OQ-45.2 (Outcome Questionnaire)* (3rd. ed.). Wilmington, DE: American Professional Credentialling Services.

Lambert, M. J., & Ogles, B. M. (2004). The efficacy and effectiveness of psychotherapy. In M. J. Lambert (Ed.), *Bergin and Garfield's handbook of psychotherapy and behavior change* (5th ed., pp. 139–193). New York, NY: Wiley.

Lambert, M. J., Shapiro, D. A., & Bergin, A. E. (1986). The effectiveness of psychotherapy. In S. L. Garfield & A. E. Bergin (Eds.), *Handbook of psychotherapy and behavior change* (pp. 157–212). New York, NY: Wiley.

Lambert, M. J., Whipple, J. L., Smart, D. W., Vermeersch, D. A., Nielsen, S. L., & Hawkins, E. J. (2001). The effects of providing therapists with feedback on patient progress during psychotherapy: Are outcomes enhanced? *Psychotherapy Research, 11*, 49-68. http://doi.org/10.1080/713663852

Lambert, M. J., Whipple, J. L., Vermeersch, D. A., Smart, D. W., Hawkins, E. J., Nielsen, S. L., & Goates, M. (2002). Enhancing psychotherapy outcomes via providing feedback on client progress: A replication. *Clinical Psychology and Psychotherapy, 9*, 91–103. http://doi.org/10.1002/cpp.324

Lange, A., van de Ven, J. Schrieken, B., & Smit, M. (2004). "Interapy" Burn-out: Prävention und Behandlung von Burn-out über das Internet ["Interapy" burnout: Prevention and treament of burnout through the Internet]. *Verhaltenstherapie, 14*, 190–199. http://doi.org/10.1159/000080915

Lawson, D. (1994). Identifying pretreatment change. *Journal of Counseling and Development, 72*, 244–248. http://doi.org/10.1002/j.1556-6676.1994.tb00929.x

LeDoux, J. E. (2000). Emotion circuits in the brain. *Annual Review in Neuroscience, 23*, 155–184. http://doi.org/10.1146/annurev.neuro.23.1.155

Leist, K.H. (1999). Synergetische Lehr-Lernprozesse des Bewegungssystems [Synergetic teaching and learning processes of the motoric system]. In K. Mainzer (Ed.), *Komplexe Systeme und Nichtlineare Dynamik in Natur und Gesellschaft* (pp. 207–221). Berlin, Germany: Springer.

Levitt, H. M., Butler, M., & Hill, T. (2006). What clients feel helpful in psychotherapy: Developing principles for facilitating moment-to-moment change. *Journal of Counseling Psychology, 53*, 314–324. http://doi.org/10.1037/0022-0167.53.3.314

Lewin, K. (1963). *Feldtheorie in den Sozialwissenschaften* [Field theory in the social sciences]. Bern, Switzerland: Huber.

Liebovitch, L. S., Peluso, P. R., Norman, M. D., Su, J., & Gottman, J. M. (2011). Mathematical model of the dynamics of psychotherapy. *Cognition and Neurodynamics, 5*, 265–275. http://doi.org/10.1007/s11571-011-9157-x

Lovibond, S. H., & Lovibond, P. F. (1995). *Manual for the Depression Anxiety Stress Scales*. Sydney, Australia: Psychology Foundation.

Luborsky, L., Singer, B., & Luborsky, L. (1975). Comparative studies of psychotherapies: Is it true that "Everyone has one and all must have prizes"? *Archives of General Psychiatry, 42*, 53–65.

Ludewig, K. (2011). Psychische Systeme – ein nützliches Konzept für die systemische Praxis? [Mental systems – a useful concept for systemic practice?]. *Familiendynamik, 36*, 222–238.

Luhmann, N. (1984). *Soziale Systeme* [Social systems]. Reinbek, Germany: Rowohlt.

Lutz, W., Böhnke, J.R., & Köck, K. (2010). Lending an ear to feedback systems: Evaluation of recovery and non-response in psychotherapy in a German outpatient setting. *Community Mental Health Journal, 47*, 311–317. http://doi.org/10.1007/s10597-010-9307-3

Mahoney, M. J. (1991). *Human change processes. The scientific foundation of psychotherapy*. New York, NY: Basic Books.

Markram, H., Lübke, J., Frotscher, M., & Sakmann, B. (1997). Regulation of synaptic efficacy by coincidence of postsynaptic APs and EPSPs. *Science, 275*, 213–215. http://doi.org/10.1126/science.275.5297.213

Martin, D. J., Garske, J. P., & Davis, K. M. (2000). Relation of the therapeutic alliance with outcome and other variables: A meta-analytic review. *Journal of Consulting and Clinical Psychology, 68*, 438–450. http://doi.org/10.1037/0022-006X.68.3.438

Mathiak, K. &., & Weisskopf, N. (2011). Neurofeedback mit Echtzeit-fMRT [Neurofeedback with real-time fMRT]. In G. Schiepek (Ed.), *Neurobiologie der Psychotherapie* (2nd ed., pp. 593–605). Stuttgart, Germany: Schattauer.

Menzies, L., Chamberlain, S. R., Laird, A. R., Thelen, S. M., Sahakian, B. J., & Bullmore, E. T. (2008). Integrating evidence from neuroimaging and neuropsychological studies of obsessive-compulsive disorder: The orbitofronto-striatal model revisited. *Neuroscience and Biobehavior Reviews, 32*, 525–549. http://doi.org/10.1016/j.neubiorev.2007.09.005

Miller, S. D. (2012). *Why most therapists are just average (and how we can improve)*. Interview by Tony Rousmaniere. Retrieved from http://www.psychotherapy.net/interview/scott-miller-interview

Miller, S. D., Duncan, B. L., Brown, J., Sorrell, R., & Chalk, M. B. (2006). Using formal client feedback to improve retention and outcome: Making ongoing real-time assessment feasible. *Journal of Brief Therapy, 5*, 5–22.

Miller, S. D., Duncan, B. L., & Hubble, M. A. (1997). *Escape from babble. Toward a unifying language for psychotherapy practice*. New York, NY: Norton.

Miller, S. D., Hubble, M. A., & Duncan, B. L. (Eds.) (1996). *Handbook of solution-focused brief therapy*. San Francisco, CA: Jossey Bass.

Miller, W. R., & C'de Baca, J. (2001). *Quantum change*. New York, NY: Guilford Press.

Molenaar, P. C. M. (2013). On the necessity to use person-specific data analysis approaches in psychology. *European Journal of Developmental Psychology, 10*, 29–39.

Newnham, E. A., Hooke, G. R. & Page, A. C. (2010). Monitoring treatment response and outcomes using the World Health Organization's Wellbeing Index in psychiatric care. *Journal of Affective Disorders, 122*, 133–138. http://doi.org/10.1016/j.jad.2009.06.005

Norcross, J. C. (Ed.). (2002). *Psychotherapy relationships that work: Therapist contributions and responsiveness to patients*. New York, NY: Oxford University Press.

Norcross, J. C. (2006). Integrating self-help into psychotherapy: 16 practical suggestions. *Professional Psychology: Research and Practice, 37*, 683–693. http://doi.org/10.1037/0735-7028.37.6.683

Norcross, J. C. (2010). The therapeutic relationship. In B. Duncan, S. Miller, B. Wampold, & M. Hubble (Eds.), *The heart and soul of change* (2nd ed., pp. 113–141). Washington, DC: American Psychological Association.

Norcross, J. C., & Goldfried, M. R. (Eds.). (1992). *Handbook of psychotherapy integration.* New York, NY: Basic Books.

Norcross, J. C., & Lambert, M. J. (2005). The therapy relationship. In J. C. Norcross, L. E. Beutler, & R. F. Levant (Eds.), *Evidence-based practices in mental health: Debate and dialogue on the fundamental questions* (pp. 208–218). Washington, DC: American Psychological Association.

Orlinsky, D.E., Grawe, K., & Parks, B. (1994). Process and outcome in psychotherapy – noch einmal. In A. E. Bergin & S. L. Garfield (Eds.), *Handbook of psychotherapy and behavior change* (4th ed., pp. 270–376). New York, NY: Wiley.

Orlinsky, D. E., Ronnestad, M. H., & Willutzki, U. (2004). Fifty years of psychotherapy process-outcome research: Continuity and change. In M. J. Lambert (Ed.), *Bergin and Garfield's handbook of psychotherapy and behavior change* (5th ed., pp. 307–390). New York, NY: Wiley.

Orsucci, F., Giuliani, A., Webber Jr., C., Zbilut, J., Fonagy, P., & Mazza, M. (2006). Combinatiorics and synchronization in natural semiotics. *Physica A, 361*, 665–676.

Osipov, G. V., Kurths, J., & Zhou, C. (2007). *Synchronization in oscillatory networks.* Berlin, Germany: Springer. http://doi.org/10.1007/978-3-540-71269-5

Pawlik, K. (Ed.) (1976). *Diagnose der Diagnostik* [Diagnosing diagnostics]. Stuttgart, Germany: Klett.

Peluso, P. R., Liebovitch, L. S., Gottman, J. M., Norman, M. D., & Su, J. (2012). A mathematical model of psychotherapy: An investigation using dynamic non-linear equations to model the therapeutic relationship. *Psychotherapy Research, 22*, 40–55. http://doi.org/10.1080/10503307.2011.622314

Pennebaker, J. W., & Chung, C. K. (2007). Expressive writing, emotional upheavals, and health. In H. Friedman & R. Silver (Eds.), *Handbook of health psychology* (pp. 263–284). New York, NY: Oxford University Press.

Petzold, H. (2003). *Integrative Therapie* [Integrative therapy] (2nd ed.). Paderborn, Germany: Junfermann.

Pikovski, A., Rosenblum, M., & Kurths, J. (2001). *Synchronization. An universal concept in nonlinear sciences.* Cambridge, UK: Cambridge University Press. http://doi.org/10.1017/CBO9780511755743

Pincus, D. (2009). Coherence, complexity, and information flow: Self-organizing processes in psychotherapy. In S. Guastello, M. Koopmans, & D. Pincus (Eds.), *Chaos and complexity in psychology. The theory of nonlinear dynamical systems* (pp. 335–369). New York, NY: Cambridge University Press.

Popovych, O. V., Hauptmann, C., & Tass, P. A. (2006). Control of neural synchrony by nonlinear delayed feedback. *Biological Cybernetics, 95*, 69–85. http://doi.org/10.1007/s00422-006-0066-8

Prochaska, J. O., Norcross, J. C., & DiClemente, C. C. (1994). *Changing for good.* New York, NY: Morrow.

Reddemann, L. (2001). *Imagination als heilsame Kraft. Zur Behandlung von Traumafolgen mit ressourcenorientierten Verfahren* [Imagination as healing force: The treatment of trauma sequels with resource-oriented techniques]. Stuttgart, Germany: Pfeiffer bei Klett-Cotta.

Reese, R. J., Norsworthy, L. A., & Rowlands, S. (2009). Does a continuous feedback system improve psychotherapy outcome? *Psychotherapy, 46*, 418–431. http://doi.org/10.1037/a0017901

Reinecker, H. (1987). *Grundlagen der Verhaltenstherapie* [Basic principles of behavior therapy]. München, Germany: PVU.

Richter, H. E. (1962). *Eltern, Kind und Neurose* [Parents, children, and neurosis]. Stuttgart, Germany: Klett.

Richter, H. E. (1970). *Patient Familie* [Patient family]. Reinbek, Germany: Rowohlt.

Rief, W., & Birbaumer, N. (2006). *Biofeedback: Grundlagen, Indikationen, Kommunikation, praktisches Vorgehen in der Therapie* [Biofeedback: Principles, indications, communication, practical approaches in therapy] (2nd ed.). Stuttgart, Germany: Schattauer.

Rizzolatti, G., & Craighero, L. (2004). The mirror neuron system. *Annual Reviews in Neuroscience, 27*, 169–192. http://doi.org/10.1146/annurev.neuro.27.070203.144230

Robinson, L. A., Berman, J. S., & Neimeyer, R. A. (1990). Psychotherapy for the treatment of depression: A comprehensive review of controlled outcome research. *Psychological Bulletin, 108*, 30–49. http://doi.org/10.1037/0033-2909.108.1.30

Rosenzweig, S. (1936). Some implicit common factors in diverse methods of psychotherapy: "At last the Dodo said: 'Everybody has won and all must have prizes.'" *American Journal of Orthopsychiatry, 6*, 412–415. http://doi.org/10.1111/j.1939-0025.1936.tb05248.x

Ruf, G. D. (2005). *Systemische Psychiatrie. Ein ressourcenorientiertes Lehrbuch* [Systemic psychiatry: A resource-oriented textbook]. Stuttgart, Germany: Klett-Cotta.

Rufer, M. (2012). *Erfasse komplex, handle einfach: Systemische Psychotherapie als Praxis der Selbstorganisation* [Capture complexity, treat simply: Systemic psychotherapy as the practice of self-organization]. Göttingen, Germany: Vandenhoeck & Ruprecht.

Ruiz, S., Lee, S., Soekadar, S. R., Caria, A., Veit, R., Kircher, T., … Sitaram, R. (2011). Acquired self-control of insula cortex modulates emotion recognition and brain network connectivity in schizophrenia. *Human Brain Mapping, 34*, 200–212. http://doi.org/10.1002/hbm.21427

Sachse, R. (1992). *Zielorientierte Gesprächstherapie* [Goal-oriented client-centered therapy]. Göttingen, Germany: Hogrefe.

Schepank, H. (1995). *BSS. Der Beeinträchtigungs-Schwere-Score. Ein Instrument zur Bestimmung der Schwere einer psychogenen Erkrankung. Manual und Testmappe* [BSS: The Disorder Severity Score: An instrument for measuring the severity of a psychogenic illness]. Göttingen, Germany: Beltz Test.

Schiepek, G. (1986). *Systemische Diagnostik in der Klinischen Psychologie* [Systemic assessment in clinical psychology]. Weinheim, Germany: Beltz/PVU.

Schiepek, G. (1991). *Systemtheorie der Klinischen Psychologie* [System theory in clinical psychology]. Braunschweig, Germany: Vieweg. http://doi.org/10.1007/978-3-322-90554-3

Schiepek, G. (2006). Die neuronale Selbstorganisation von Persönlichkeit und Identität [The neuronal self-organization of personality and identity]. *Psychotherapie, 11*, 192–201.

Schiepek, G. (2009). Complexity and nonlinear dynamics in psychotherapy. *European Review, 17*, 331–356. http://doi.org/10.1017/S1062798709000763

Schiepek, G. (2011) (Ed.). *Neurobiologie der Psychotherapie* [The neurobiology of psychotherapy] (2nd ed.). Stuttgart, Germany: Schattauer.

Schiepek, G., & Aichhorn, W. (2013). Real-Time Monitoring in der Psychotherapie [Real-time monitoring in psychotherapy]. *Psychotherapie, Psychosomatik und medizinische Psychologie, 63*, 39–47.

Schiepek, G., Aichhorn, W., & Strunk, G. (2012). Der Therapie-Prozessbogen (TPB). Faktorenstruktur und psychometrische Daten [The Therapy Process Questionnaire (TPQ). Factor structure and psychometric data]. *Zeitschrift für Psychosomatische Medizin und Psychotherapie, 58*, 257–266. http://doi.org/10.13109/zptm.2012.58.3.257

Schiepek, G., & Cremers, S. (2003). Ressourcenorientierung und Ressourcendiagnostik in der Psychotherapie [Resource-orientation and resource diagnostics in psychotherapy]. In H. Schemmel & J. Schaller (Eds.), *Ressourcen. Ein Hand- und Lesebuch zur therapeutischen Arbeit* [Resources: A textbook for therapeutic work] (pp. 147–193). Tübingen, Germany: DGVT.

Schiepek, G., Eckert, H., Honermann, H., & Weihrauch, S. (2001). Ordnungswandel in komplexen dynamischen Systemen: Das systemische Paradigma jenseits der Therapieschulen [Order transitions in complex dynamic systems: The systemic paradigm beyond schools of therapy]. *Hypnose & Kognition, 18*, 89–117.

Schiepek, G., Kowalik, Z. J., Schütz, A., Köhler, M., Richter, K., Strunk, G., … Elbert, T. (1997). Psychotherapy as a chaotic process I. Coding the client-therapist-interaction by means of sequential plan analysis and the search for chaos: A stationary approach. *Psychotherapy Research, 7*, 173–194. http://doi.org/10.1080/10503309712331331953

Schiepek, G., & Perlitz, V. (2009). Self-organization in clinical psychology. In R. A. Meyers (Ed.). *Encyclopedia of complexity and systems science* (pp. 7991–8009). New York, NY: Springer.

Schiepek, G., & Strunk, G. (2010). The identification of critical fluctuations and phase transitions in short term and coarse-grained time series – a method for the real-time monitoring of human change processes. *Biological Cybernetics, 102*, 197–207. http://doi.org/10.1007/s00422-009-0362-1

Schiepek, G., Tominschek, I., Heinzel, S., Aigner, M., Dold, M., Unger, A., … Karch, S. (2013). Discontinuous patterns of brain activation in the psychotherapy process of obsessive-compulsive disorder: Converging results from repeated fMRI and daily self-reports. *PloS ONE, 8*(8), e71863 http://doi.org/10.1371/journal.pone.0071863

Schiepek, G., Tominschek, I., & Heinzel, S. (2014). Self-organization in psychotherapy: Testing the synergetic model of change processes. *Frontiers in Psychology for Clinical Settings, 5*, Article 1089, 1–11.

Schiepek, G., Tominschek, I., Karch, S., Lutz, J., Mulert, C., Meindl, T., & Pogarell, O. (2009). A controlled single case study with repeated fMRI measures during the treatment of a patient with obsessive-compulsive disorder: Testing the nonlinear dynamics approach to psychotherapy. *The World Journal of Biological Psychiatry, 10*, 658–668. http://doi.org/10.1080/15622970802311829

Schiepek, G., Wegener, C., Wittig, D., & Harnischmacher, G. (1998). *Synergie und Qualität in Organisationen. Ein Fensterbilderbuch* [Synergy and quality in organizations]. Tübingen, Germany: DGVT.

Schiepek, G., Zellweger, A., Kronberger, H., Aichhorn, W., & Leeb, W. (2011). Psychotherapie [Psychotherapy]. In G. Schiepek (Ed.), *Neurobiologie der Psychotherapie* (2nd ed., pp. 567–592). Stuttgart, Germany: Schattauer.

Schiersmann, C., & Thiel, H. U. (2012). Beratung als Förderung von Selbstorganisationsprozessen – eine Theorie jenseits von "Schulen" und "Formaten" [Counseling as facilitation of self-organizing processes – a theory beyond "schools" and "approaches"]. In C. Schiersmann & H. U. Thiel (Eds.), *Beratung als Förderung von Selbstorganisations-prozessen* (pp. 132–163). Göttingen, Germany: Vandenhoeck & Ruprecht.

Schmid-Schönbein, H. (1996). Physiological synergetics: A holistic concept concerning phase jumps in the behaviour of driven nonlinear systems. In R. Greger & U. Windhorst (Eds.), *Comprehensive human physiology. Vol. 1* (pp. 43–67). Berlin, Germany: Springer.

Schmidt, G. (2005). *Einführung in die hypno-systemische Therapie und Beratung* [Intro-duction to hyno-systemic therapy and counseling]. Heidelberg, Germany: Carl Auer.

Schulman, J. J., Cancro, R., Lowe, S., Lu, F., Walton, K. D., & Llinas, R. R. (2011). Imag-ing of thalamocortical dysrhythmia in neuropsychiatry. *Frontiers in Human Neurosci-ence, 5*, 69. http://doi.org/10.3389/fnhum.2011.00069

Schweitzer, J., & von Schlippe, A. (2009). *Lehrbuch der systemischen Therapie und Be-ratung II. Das störungsspezifische Wissen* [Textbook of systemic therapy and coun-seling II. Disorder-specific knowledge] (3rd ed.). Göttingen, Germany: Vandenhoeck & Ruprecht.

Schwing, R., & Fryszer, A. (2006). *Systemisches Handwerk* [Systemic tools]. Göttingen, Germany: Vandenhoeck & Ruprecht.

Sexton, T. L., Alexander, J. F., & Mease, A. L. (2004). Levels of evidence for the models and mechanisms of therapeutic change in family and couple therapy. In M. J. Lambert (Ed.), *Bergin and Garfield's handbook of psychotherapy and behavior change* (5th ed., pp. 590–646). New York, NY: Wiley.

Shadish, W. R., & Baldwin, S. A. (2002). Meta-analysis of MFT interventions. In D. H. Sprenkle (Ed.), *Effectiveness research in marriage and family therapy* (pp. 339–379). Alexandria, VA: American Association of Marriage and Family Therapy.

Shadish, W. R., & Baldwin, S. A. (2003). Meta-analysis of MFT interventions. *Journal of Marital and Family Therapy, 29*, 547–570. http://doi.org/10.1111/j.1752-0606.2003.tb01694.x

Shadish, W. R., Montgomery, L. M., Wilson, P., Wilson, M. R., Bright, I., & Okwumabua, T. (1993). Effects of family and marital psychotherapies: A meta-analysis. *Journal of Consult-ing and Clinical Psychology, 61*, 992–1002. http://doi.org/10.1037/0022-006X.61.6.992

Shapiro, D. A., Harper, H., Startup, M., Reynolds, S., Bird, D., & Suokas, A. (1994). The high-water mark of the drug metaphor. A meta-analytic critique of process-outcome research. In R. L. Russell (Ed.), *Reassessing psychotherapy research* (pp. 1–35). New York, NY: Guilford Press.

Shapiro, D. A., & Shapiro, D. (1982). Meta-analysis of comparative therapy outcome research: A critical appraisal. *Behavioural Psychotherapy, 10*, 4–25. http://doi.org/10.1017/S0141347300008181

Shaw, B. F., Elkin, I., Yamaguchi, J., Olmsted, M., Vallis, T. M., Dobson, K. S. … Imber, S. D. (1999). Therapist competence ratings in relation to clinical outcome in cognitive therapy of depression. *Journal of Consulting and Clinical Psychology, 67*, 837–846. http://doi.org/10.1037/0022-006X.67.6.837

Siegel, M., Donner, T. H., & Engel, K. A. (2012). Spectral fingerprints of large-scale neu-ronal interactions. *Nature Reviews Neuroscience, 13*, 121–134.

Singer, W. (2011). Das Gehirn – ein komplexes, sich selbst organisierendes System [The brain – a complex self-organizing system]. In G. Schiepek (Ed.), *Neurobiologie der Psychotherapie* (2nd ed., pp. 133–141). Stuttgart, Germany: Schattauer.

Skodol, A. E., Bender, D. S., Pagano, M. E., Shea, M. T., Yen, S., Sanislow, C.A., ... Gunderson, J. G. (2007). Positive childhood experiences: Resilience and recovery from personality disorder in early adulthood. *Journal of Clinical Psychiatry, 68*, 1102–1108. http://doi.org/10.4088/JCP.v68n0719

Sloane, R. B., Staples, F. R., Cristol, A. H., Yorkston, N. J. I., & Whipple, K. (1975). *Short-term analytically oriented psychotherapy versus behaviour therapy*. Cambridge, MA: Harvard University Press. http://doi.org/10.4159/harvard.9780674365063

Smith, M. L., & Glass, G. V. (1977). Meta-analysis of psychotherapy outcome studies. *American Psychologist, 32*, 752–760.

Smith, M. L., Glass, G. V., & Miller, T. I. (1980). *The benefits of psychotherapy*. Baltimore, MD: Johns Hopkins University Press.

Sneed, J. D. (1979). *The logical structure of mathematical physics* (2nd ed.). Dordrecht, The Netherlands: Reidel. http://doi.org/10.1007/978-94-009-9522-2

Sparks, J. A., & Duncan, B. L. (2010). Common factors in couple and family therapy: Must all have prizes? In B. Duncan, S. Miller, B. Wampold, & M. Hubble (Eds.), *The heart and soul of change* (2nd ed., pp. 357–391). Washington, DC: American Psychological Association.

Spek, V., Cuijpers, P., Nyklíček, I., Riper, H., Keyzer, J., & Pop, V. (2007). Internet-based cognitive behaviour therapy for symptoms of depression and anxiety: A meta-analysis. *Psychological Medicine, 37*, 319–328. http://doi.org/10.1017/S0033291706008944

Stadler, M., & Kruse, P. (1990). The self-organization perspective in cognition research. Historical remarks and new experimental approaches. In H. Haken & M. Stadler (Eds.), *Synergetics of cognition* (pp. 32–52). Berlin, Germany: Springer.

Stegmüller, W. (1973). *Theorie und Erfahrung. Zweiter Halbband: Theorienstrukturen und Theoriendynamik* [Theory and experience. 2nd Subvolume: Theory structure and theory dynamics]. Berlin, Germany: Springer. http://doi.org/10.1007/978-3-662-00224-7

Stegmüller, W. (1979). *Rationale Rekonstruktion von Wissenschaft und ihrem Wandel* [The rational reconstruction of science and its evolution]. Stuttgart, Germany: Reclam.

Stiles, W. B, Leach, C., Barkham, M., Lucock, M., Iveson, S., Shapiro, D., ... Hardy, G. (2003). Early sudden gains in psychotherapy under routine clinic conditions: Practice-based evidence. *Journal of Consulting and Clinical Psychology, 71*, 14–21. http://doi.org/10.1037/0022-006X.71.1.14

Stiles, W. B., Shapiro, D. A., & Harper, H. (1994). Finding the way from process to outcome: Blind alleys and unmarked trails. In R. L. Russell (Ed.), *Reassessing psychotherapy research* (pp. 36–64). New York, NY: Guilford.

Strunk, G., & Schiepek, G. (2002). Dynamische Komplexität in der Therapeut-Klient-Interaktion [Dynamic complexity in the therapist–client interaction]. *Psychotherapeut, 47*, 291–300. http://doi.org/10.1007/s00278-002-0242-9

Strunk, G., & Schiepek, G. (2006). *Systemische Psychologie. Einführung in die komplexen Grundlagen menschlichen Verhaltens* [Systemic psychology. Introduction to the complexity of human behavior]. Heidelberg, Germany: Spektrum Akademischer Verlag.

Stulz, N., Lutz, W., Leach, C., Lucock, M., & Barkham, M. (2007). Shapes of early change in psychotherapy under routine outpatient conditions. *Journal of Consulting and Clinical Psychology, 75*, 864–874. http://doi.org/10.1037/0022-006X.75.6.864

Tang, T., & DeRubeis, R. (1999a). Sudden gains and critical sessions in cognitive-behavioral therapy for depression. *Journal of Consulting and Clinical Psychology, 67*, 894–904. http://doi.org/10.1037/0022-006X.67.6.894

Tang, T., & DeRubeis, R. (1999b). Reconsidering rapid early response in cognitive behavioral therapy for depression. *Clinical Psychology: Science and Practice, 6*, 283–284.

Tang, T., DeRubeis, R., Beberman, R., & Pham, T. (2005). Cognitive changes, critical sessions, and sudden gains in cognitive-behavioral therapy for depression. *Journal of Consulting and Clinical Psychology, 73*, 168–172. http://doi.org/10.1037/0022-006X.73.1.168

Tang, T., DeRubeis, R., Hollon, S., Amsterdam, J., & Shelton, R. (2007). Sudden gains in cognitive-behavioral therapy of depression and depression relapse/recurrence. *Journal of Consulting and Clinical Psychology, 75*, 404–408. http://doi.org/10.1037/0022-006X.75.3.404

Tang, T., Luborsky, L., & Andrusyna, T. (2002). Sudden gains in recovering from depression: Are they also found in psychotherapies other than cognitive-behavioral therapy? *Journal of Consulting and Clinical Psychology, 70*, 444–447. http://doi.org/10.1037/0022-006X.70.2.444

Tass, P. A. (2003). A model of desynchronizing deep brain stimulation with a demand-controlled coordinated reset of neural subpopulations. *Biological Cybernetics, 89*, 81–88. http://doi.org/10.1007/s00422-003-0425-7

Tass, P. A., Adamchic, I., Freund, H. J., von Stackelberg, T., & Hauptmann, C. (2012). Counteracting tinnitus by acoustic coordinated reset neuromodulation. *Restorative Neurology and Neuroscience, 30*, 137–159.

Tass, P. A., & Hauptmann, C. (2007). Therapeutic modulation of synaptic connectivity with desynchronizing brain stimulation. *International Journal of Psychophysiologiy, 64*, 53–61. http://doi.org/10.1016/j.ijpsycho.2006.07.013

Tass, P. A., & Majtanik, M. (2006). Long-term anti-kindling effects of desynchronizing brain stimulation: A theoretical study. *Biological Cybernetics, 94*, 58–66. http://doi.org/10.1007/s00422-005-0028-6

Tass, P., & Popovych, O. V. (2012). Unlearning tinnitus-related cerebral synchrony with acoustic coordinated reset stimulation: Theoretical concept and modelling. *Biological Cybernetics, 106*, 27–36. http://doi.org/10.1007/s00422-012-0479-5

Tass, P. A., Smirnov, D., Karavaev, A., Barnikol, U., Barnikol, T., Adamchic, I., … Bezruchko, B. (2010). The causal relationship between subcortical local field potential oscillations and Parkinsonian resting tremor. *Journal of Neural Engineering, 7*, 016009 http://doi.org/10.1088/1741-2560/7/1/016009

Tatzer, E., & Schubert, M. T. (1997). Systemtherapie im Kinderheim [System therapy in children's homes]. In L. Reiter, E. J. Brunner, & S. Reiter-Theil (Ed.), *Von der Familientherapie zur systemischen Perspektive* (2nd ed., pp. 143–154). Berlin, Heidelberg, Germany: Springer.

Tedeschi, J. T., & Felson, R. B. (1994). *Violence, aggression, and coercive actions.* Washington, DC: American Psychological Association. http://doi.org/10.1037/10160-000

Tedeschi, J. T., Park, C. L., & Calhoun, L. G. (Eds.) (1998). *Posttraumatic growth.* Mahwah, NJ: Erlbaum.

Timulak, L. (2010). Significant events in psychotherapy: An update of research findings. *Psychology and psychotherapy: Theory, research, and practice, 83*, 421–447. http://doi.org/10.1348/147608310X499404

Tretter, F., & Grüsser-Sinopoli, S. M. (2011). Sucht und Suchttherapie [Addiction and addiction therapy]. In G. Schiepek (Ed.), *Neurobiologie der Psychotherapie* (2nd ed., pp. 486–508). Stuttgart, Germany: Schattauer.

Tritt, K., von Heymann, F., Zaudig, M., Zacharias, I., Söllner, W., & Löw, T. (2007). *Die Entwicklung des Fragebogens ICD-10-Symptom-Rating (ISR) – Kurzbeschreibung der Pilotversion 1.0 und der Version 2.0* [The development of the ICD-10-Symptom-Rating (ISR) questionnaire – a short description of the pilot version 1.0 and version 2.0]. Regensburg, Germany: Institut für Qualitätsentwicklung in der Psychotherapie und Psychosomatik.

Tryon, G. S., & Winograd, G. (2011). Goal consensus and collaboration. *Psychotherapy, 48*, 50–57. http://doi.org/10.1037/a0022061

Ulrich, C. (2011). *Paartherapie-Prozessforschung. Entwicklung und Anwendung einer innovativen Forschungsstrategie* [Couple therapy process research. Development and application of an innovative research strategy]. (Doctoral dissertation). Ludwig Maximilians University Munich, Germany.

Vittengl, J., Clark, L., & Jarrett, R. (2005). Validity of sudden gains in acute phase treatment of depression. *Journal of Consulting and Clinical Psychology, 73*, 173–182. http://doi.org/10.1037/0022-006X.73.1.173

von Uexküll, T., Adler, R. H., Herrmann, J. M., Köhle, K., Schonecke, O. W., & Wesiack, W. (Ed.). (2011). *Psychosomatische Medizin* [Psychosomatic medicine] (7th ed.). München, Germany: Urban & Fischer/Elsevier.

Wahl, A. (2012). Generische Prinzipien in der beruflichen Beratung – Konkretisierung und Fallbeispiel [Generic principles in career counseling – Concretization and case study]. In C. Schiersmann & H. U. Thiel (Eds.), *Beratung als Förderung von Selbstorganisationsprozessen* (pp. 104–131). Göttingen, Germany: Vandenhoeck & Ruprecht.

Walter, J. L., & Peller, J. E. (1992). *Becoming solution-focused in brief therapy*. New York, NY: Bruner & Mazel.

Wampold, B. E. (2001). *The great psychotherapy debate. Models, methods, and findings*. Mahwah, NJ: Erlbaum.

Wampold, B. E. (2010). The research evidence for common factors models: A historically situated perspective. In B. Duncan, S. Miller, B. Wampold, & M. Hubble (Eds.), *The heart and soul of change* (2nd ed., pp. 49–82). Washington, DC: American Psychological Association.

Wampold, B. E., Minami, T., Baskin, T. W., & Tierney, S. C. (2002). A meta-(re)analysis of the effects of cognitive therapy versus "other therapies" for depression. *Journal of Affective Disorders, 68*, 159–165. http://doi.org/10.1016/S0165-0327(00)00287-1

Wampold, B. E., Mondin, G. W., Moody, M., Stich, F., Benson, K., & Ahn, H. (1997). A meta-analysis of outcome studies comparing bona fide psychotherapies: Empirically, "All must have prizes." *Psychological Bulletin, 122*, 203–215. http://doi.org/10.1037/0033-2909.122.3.203

Webb, C. A., DeRubeis, R. J., & Barber, J. P. (2010). Therapist adherence/competence and treatment outcome: A meta-analytic review. *Journal of Consulting and Clinical Psychology, 78*, 200–211. http://doi.org/10.1037/a0018912

Webber, C. L., & Zbilut, J. P. (1994). Dynamical assessment of physiological systems and states using recurrence plot strategies. *Journal of Applied Physiology, 76*, 965–973.

Weiner-Davies, M., de Shazer, S., & Gingerich, W. (1987). Building on pretreatment change to construct the therapeutic solution: An exploratory study. *Journal of Marital and Family Therapy, 13*, 359–364. http://doi.org/10.1111/j.1752-0606.1987.tb00717.x

Weiss, J. (1993). *How psychotherapy works: Process and technique*. New York, NY: Guilford.

Weiss, T. (1988). *Familientherapie ohne Familie: Kurztherapie mit Einzelpatienten* [Family therapy without the family: Short therapy for individual patients]. Munich, Germany: Kösel.

Westmeyer, H. (1972). *Logik der Diagnostik* [The logic of diagnostics]. Stuttgart, Germany: Kohlhammer.

Westmeyer, H. (1979). Die rationale Rekonstruktion einiger Aspekte psychologischer Praxis [The rational reconstruction of some aspects of psychological practice]. In H. Albert & K. H. Stapf (Eds.), *Theorie und Erfahrung. Beiträge zur Grundlagenproblematik in den Sozialwissenschaften*. Stuttgart, Germany: Klett.

Westmeyer, H. (1984). Diagnostik und therapeutische Entscheidung: Begründungsprobleme [Diagnostic and therapeutic decisions: Problems in the justification of decisions]. In G. Jüttemann (Ed.), *Neue Aspekte klinisch-psychologischer Diagnostik* (pp. 77–101). Göttingen, Germany: Hogrefe.

Westmeyer, H. (Ed.) (1992). *The structuralist program in psychology: Foundations and applications*. Kirkland, WA: Hogrefe & Huber Publishers.

Westmeyer, H. (1997). Möglichkeiten der Begründung therapeutischer Entscheidungen [Possibilites for justifying therapeutic decisions]. In F. Caspar (Ed.), *Problemanalyse in der Psychotherapie* (pp. 20–31). Tübingen, Germany: DGVT.

Wilson, G. T. (1999). Rapid response to cognitive-behavior therapy. *Clinical Psychology: Science and Practice, 6*, 289–292.

Wolfe, B. E., & Goldfried, M. R. (1988). Research on psychotherapy integration: Recommendations and conclusions from an NIMH workshop. *Journal of Consulting and Clinical Psychology, 56*, 448–451. http://doi.org/10.1037/0022-006X.56.3.448

Zanarini, M. C., Frankenburg, F. R., Hennen, J., Reich, D. B., & Silk, K. (2006). Prediction of the ten year course of borderline personality disorder. *American Journal of Psychiatry, 163*, 827–832. http://doi.org/10.1176/appi.ajp.163.5.827

Appendix

Dynamic Complexity

An algorithm of dynamic complexity is used in the SNS to identify nonstationary phenomena and critical instabilities in short- and coarse-grained time series. Dynamic complexity is the multiplicative product of a fluctuation measure and a distribution measure. Both measures are used for the analysis of discrete time series data with known theoretical data ranges. Let x_t represent the value of a variable measured at time t on the basis of a constant and discrete time interval (scanning frequency, e.g., one observation per day). Values are represented on the basis of a constant unit with theoretical data range s between the theoretical minimum x_{min} and the theoretical maximum x_{max} of x. The fluctuation measure (F) is sensitive to the amplitude and frequency of changes in a time signal, and the distribution measure (D) scans the scattering of values or system states realized within the theoretical data range of possible values or system states. In order to identify nonstationarity, the two measures are calculated within a data-window moving over the time series.

Fluctuation Intensity

The fluctuation algorithm is applied to segments of discrete time series. These segments are defined by the width of a moving window that can be fixed arbitrarily. The window runs over the whole time series and results in a continuous fluctuation intensity measure F. All measurement points within the window are subdivided into periods with cut-off points defined by changes in slope (points of return k). Trends can be: "increasing", "decreasing", or "no change" (Figure 35). The difference between the values x_n at the points of return k is taken irrespective of the sign – in absolute terms: $y_i = \left| x_{n_{k+1}} - x_{n_k} \right|$ – and is divided by the duration of the period (i.e., the number of data points within the period from one point of return k to the next one $k+1$). By this, the change rate is related to its duration, and F is sensitive to the frequency as well as to the amplitude of the fluctuation. Theses fractions are summed up within the window. In order to normalize the fluctuation intensity, the result is related to the greatest possible fluctuation which is given by the maximum amount of change within a minimum duration. This is the sum of the differences between the lowest and the highest value of the available range between one and the next measurement point. The formula results in a normalized fluctuation intensity $0 \le F \le 1$:

$$F = \frac{\displaystyle\sum_{i=1}^{I} \frac{y_i}{(n_{k+1} - n_k)}}{s(m-1)}$$

with

$y_i = \left| x_{n_{k+1}} - x_{n_k} \right|$

x_n nth value of the time series

k points of return (number of changes in slope of the data sequence)

i periods between points of return

I   total number of such periods within the window

m   number of measurement points within a moving window

m–1   number of intervals between all measurement points of a window

$s = x_{max} - x_{min}$ with x_{min} smallest value of the scale, x_{max} largest value of the scale.

One can immediately derive that $\sum_{i=1}^{I} \dfrac{y_i}{n_{k+1} - n_k} \leq s(m-1)$, so $0 \leq F \leq 1$ (see Figure 35).

Note that $s(m-1)$ is the window area expressed in units of t and x and that s is not the empirical data range but the theoretical range of the scale.

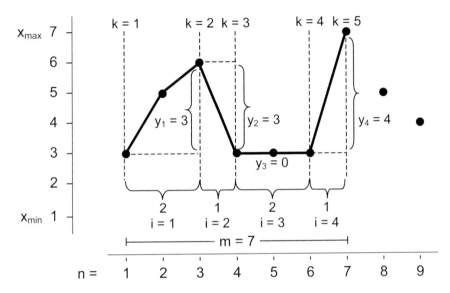

Figure 35

In this example, the *F* value is calculated as follows: The first contributor is between $k = 1$ and $k = 2$, a difference of 3 (since $x_1 = 3$, $x_3 = 6$), divided by 2 (2 is the number of intervals between $k = 1$ and $k = 2$). The next contributor is between $k = 2$ and $k = 3$, a difference of 3, divided by only one interval. Next is a difference of 0 divided by 2 intervals (remains 0), and the last difference between $k = 4$ and $k = 5$ is 4, divided by 1. So we sum up 3/2 + 3/1 + 0/2 + 4/1 = 8.5. This sum is divided by the maximum of possible fluctuation, which is in this case (with the greatest number of points of return $k = 1$ to $k = 7$, and $s = (x_{max} - x_{min}) = 7 - 1 = 6$): 6/1 + 6/1 + 6/1+ 6/1 + 6/1 + 6/1 = 36. $F = 8.5/36 = .23611$.

Distribution

The degree of distribution *D* represents another aspect of dynamic complexity. Whereas *F* is at its maximum when the dynamics jump between the minimum and maximum values with greatest and equal frequency, instabilities and dynamic complexity in general are often characterised by irregularities, resulting in quite different system states. In the extreme case, the values should be irregularly and chaotically distributed across the range of the measurement scale. As a result, the degree of distribution measures the deviance of the values from an ideal equal distribution of the values across the range or measurement scale. As for the calculation of *F*, we use a moving window running through the whole process and by doing this we consider the values over the full course of the process. For the distribution measure the order of values within the moving window is irrelevant, and in a first step values are sorted in ascending order. Let x_i be the values of a variable x at the sorting position i within the moving window X which is given by:

$$X = \{x_1, x_2, x_3, \dots x_m\} \text{ with } x_1 \leq x_2 \leq x_3 \leq \dots x_m$$

In the following calculation this sorted window is compared with an artificial data set of equally distributed values. This artificial data set consists of the same number m of values arranged in ascending order in equally spaced intervals between the theoretical scale minimum and maximum. The interval I is given by $I = s / (m-1)$, $s = x_{max} - x_{min}$ and the artificial data set Y is given by:

$$Y = \{y_1 = I*1, y_2 = I*2, y_3 = I*3, \dots y_m = I*m\}$$

If the data set in X is equally distributed within the data range, then differences between values at different positions in X must be equal to the differences in Y at the same positions. To give an example, if X is perfectly equally distributed within the data range, then $\delta_{Y.2-1} = y_2 - y_1 = \delta_{X.2-1} = x_2 - x_1$. Generally the aberration Δ_{ba} of X from the ideal given in Y can be calculated for the positions a and b as follows:

$$\Delta_{ba} = \delta_{Y.b-a} - \delta_{X.b-a} \text{ with } \delta_{Y.b-a} = y_b - y_a \text{ and } \delta_{X.b-a} = x_b - x_a$$

In total the aberration $\Delta*$ is given by the following permutation of a and b.

$$\Delta* = \sum_{c=1}^{m-1} \sum_{d=c+1}^{m} \sum_{a=c}^{d-1} \sum_{b=a+1}^{d} \Delta_{ba} \Theta(\Delta_{ba})$$

The two outer sums are permutations of all combinations of c and d within the window. The inner sums of a and b are representing all combinations of positions within the interval given by c and d.

$\Theta(\Delta_{ba})$ is the Heaviside step function resulting in 1 if Δ_{ba} is a positive number; otherwise the function results in 0. Therefore, only positive aberrations are considered, because negative aberrations have the consequence of resulting in positive ones in other positions.

Hence, the distribution measurement D is given by:

$$D = 1 - \sum_{c=1}^{m-1} \sum_{d=c+1}^{m} \sum_{a=c}^{d-1} \sum_{b=a+1}^{d} \frac{\Delta_{ba} \Theta(\Delta_{ba})}{\delta_{Y.ba}}$$

One can see that D is normalized so that $0 \leq D \leq 1$, and a high value of D is the result of equally distributed measures of x within the moving window.

View all volumes at www.hogrefe.com/series/apt

Hogrefe Publishing
30 Amberwood Parkway · Ashland, OH 44805 · USA
Tel: (800) 228-3749 · Fax: (419) 281-6883
E-Mail: customerservice@hogrefe.com

Hogrefe Publishing
Merkelstr. 3 · 37085 Göttingen · Germany
Tel: +49 551 999 500 · Fax: +49 551 999 50 111
E-Mail: customerservice@hogrefe.de

Hogrefe Publishing c/o Marston Book Services Ltd
160 Eastern Ave., Milton Park · Abingdon, OX14 4SB · UK
Tel: +44 1235 465577 · Fax +44 1235 465556
direct.orders@marston.co.uk

HOGREFE

Order online at **www.hogrefe.com**
or call toll-free **(800) 228-3749** (US only)